W9-BBH-218

INSECT SEX ATTRACTANTS

INSECT SEX ATTRACTANTS

MARTIN JACOBSON

Entomology Research Division
Agricultural Research Service
U.S. Department of Agriculture
Beltsville, Maryland

with a Forword by STANLEY A. HALL

Chief, Pesticide Chemicals Research Branch
Entomology Research Division
U. S. Department of Agriculture

INTERSCIENCE PUBLISHERS
A Division of John Wiley & Sons, Inc.   *New York • London • Sydney*

SECOND PRINTING, JANUARY, 1967

To my wife, Nettie

*without whose constant urging and inspiration
this book would not have been written.*

FOREWORD

Public consciousness of the undesirable side effects (some fancied and some real) of pesticides, coupled with the pressing problem of harmful insect species becoming resistant or immune to many insecticides, has spurred research on insect attractants as a potential new method of insect control. The sex attractants have captured the imagination of the public, and have also engaged the serious attention of entomologists and chemists here and abroad. The isolation and identification of very minute amounts of sex attractants from insects can be much more readily accomplished today with new methods such as gas chromatography, carbon skeleton chromatography, and with such modern instrumentation as nuclear magnetic resonance and mass spectrometry that we now have at our command. This opens up a rich field indeed for the organic chemist. The discovery of new sex attractants has thus been greatly stimulated. Entomologists who have worked to control injurious species for decades and who may, in all likelihood, have never observed a natural atractant in operation now find that there are indeed sex attractants that they had not suspected. For example, females of the codling moth, the most destructive pest of apples, have been found only recently to possess a powerful sex attractant that lures the males. In the order Lepidoptera, sex attractants are the rule rather than the exception. Research thus far has pointed to long-chain unsaturated alcohols or esters as being typical of the structure of sex attractants present in the female moths of this order. Table 1 (pages 33–38) is of special interest in pointing up the known distribution among the insect orders of species in which there is a sex attractant present in the female to lure the males. Of the six orders of insects listed, the Lepidoptera, an order comprising well over 1,00,000 described species, has by all odds the most representatives possessing sex attractants. Future work may reveal that sex attractants can be found in certain species drawn from all the orders of the insects, which presently total about 700,000 known species. Table 2 (pages 46–48) is surprising in the number of insect species that the author lists, in which males "lure or excite" the females; these phenomena are presumably due to chemical lures or aphrodisiacs.

The chief value of this book is its thorough coverage of what is known, thus enabling those who are interested to plan more logically and systematically their future chemical and biological research in this exciting new field of natural products. Martin Jacobson has laid the groundwork for a grand endeavor which will undoubtedly attract not a few organic chemists, particularly in universities, research institutions, and Government laboratories to work on the isolation and structure determination of these sex attractants in the years ahead. Some of the future research will be academic and some of it will be highly practical, especially where synthesis of a sex attractant can be accomplished and put to work to control or eradicate an injurious insect species.

Stanley A. Hall

Chief, Pesticide Chemicals Research Branch
Entomology Research Division, U.S.D.A.

Beltsville, Maryland
January 1965

PREFACE

The extent to which sex attractants occur in the insect world is unknown, but reports which have appeared in increasing numbers within the past few years indicate that sex lures are prevalent among insect species. The list of those species in which sex attractants and excitants have been demonstrated is now quite impressive. That the insect sex attractant literature has recently grown by leaps and bounds is due in no small measure to the fascinating fact that these substances, produced by the insects themselves as a requisite to their reproduction, may be used for their destruction.

The need for a reference book on the sex atractants of insects has become increasingly apparent. Most of the basic work on the subject has as yet been described only in numerous scattered reports, although published reviews of various phases of the subject have occasionally appeared. This fact and the growing popularity of the subject have made it imperative that the published information on all phases of the subject be gathered together in one convenient place for the first time. Although this has been my aim in preparing this reference book, and I have made an effort to include in the list of references every pertinent contribution, it is possible that a few reports have not been included either because I have been unaware of their existence in obscure journals or their existence has otherwise escaped me. It is my sincere hope that this book will provide an incentive for greater discoveries in this fascinating field.

Line figures adapted from other sources have been redrawn and, in some cases, modified. Halftones are reproduced through the kindness of the publishers, with the source of each indicated. All listed references have been consulted directly. References which appeared or were noted after the manuscript was prepared have been assigned supplementary numbers, enabling me to include the literature which appeared up to a few months prior to publication.

I acknowledge a debt of gratitude to my wife, Nettie, for the bulk of the typing of the manuscript, and to my daughter, Barbara Diane, for preparing several of the line figures. A special note of thanks is due a number of the experts on insect taxonomy at the National Museum of the Smithsonian Institution, Washington, D.C., for checking many of the insect names.

                                                                    M. Jacobson

Silver Spring, Maryland
August, 1965

CONTENTS

xi

CHAPTER ONE

INTRODUCTION

"Insects have managed to persist in hostile surroundings because they have developed extraordinary adaptations or abilities, one of which is a highly specialized sense of smell. Some insects can follow unerringly an odor trail to a source of food, to host plants and animals, to the opposite sex, or to the right place to lay eggs. Because many insects depend for their survival on these odors, frequently they can be attracted by means of a chemical to a trap for detection purposes, or to a toxicant that destroys the insect, or to a substance which makes them incapable of fertile mating" (185).

Attractants may be classified as sex, food, or oviposition lures. The type of lure is inferred or deduced from insect behavior, and the assignment is frequently uncertain. A chemical is probably a sex attractant if it brings to it an insect, which then assumes a mating position. This definition therefore excludes a number of substances, mainly food attractants, that lure only one sex of an insect; these have not been considered in this presentation. The sex attractants, usually released by the female insect to lure the male, are important, if not essential, links in the process by which the opposite sexes locate each other for mating. Although odors released by female insects are usually for the purpose of attracting males from a distance, they may also serve merely to excite the male sexually before copulation. Sexual odors released by males are primarily for the purpose of sexually exciting the female, making

1

her more receptive to the male's advances; they are thus in the nature of "aphrodisiacs." These chemical messengers have also been called "assembling scents" (202) and "sex pheromones," from the Greek "pherein" (to carry) and "horman" (to excite, stimulate) (195). The term pheromone has been attacked by Kirschenblatt (209) as being etymologically incorrect, as it gives no clue to its exact derivation. Kirschenblatt (207, 208) had previously proposed the term "telergones," from the Greek "tele" (afar) and "ergon" (action), to designate all biologically active substances secreted by animals into their environment which influence other organisms ("these substances are products of external secretion and differ principally by their importance from hormones, which display their physiological action within the organism producing them") (207). Micklem (236) cited the same objection to the term "pheromone" and suggested that it be changed to "pherormone." In their reply to Micklem, Karlson and Lüscher (197) gave a new etymological explanation for their term, stating that the ending "mone" is regarded as a proper suffix used in such scientific terms as "hormones," "gamones," and "termones." "Pheromone" is now commonly used to include those substances secreted by an animal to influence the behavior of other animals of the same species (354).

The more obvious examples of insects attracting mates were discovered when males responded to caged or immobilized females, but such observations are comparatively few. Although many entomologists have been of the opinion that virtually all insect species will produce sex attractants that are species specific, numerous examples of nonspecificity are cited in this review; it is my opinion that additional examples will continue to be found with increasing investigation in this field. Detected by the insect in fantastically minute amounts, these attractants are undoubtedly among the most potent physiologically active substances known today.

Although a number of reviews have appeared, the following list treats limited segments of the field which are of interest to us (39, 40, 41, 42, 43, 59, 71, 129a, 145, 147a, 158, 160, 163, 164, 167, 176, 184, 185, 187, 194, 195, 204, 243, 264b, 272, 354, 354a).

CHAPTER TWO

OCCURRENCE AND DEMONSTRATION
OF SEX ATTRACTANTS IN THE FEMALE

As long ago as 1837 Siebold (315) recognized that a pair of appendages, sometimes colored, opening into the vagina of the females of some insect species may act as a male attractant. He surmised that the odor emitted by a female insect probably functions to entice the male, while that emitted by a male may be used as a stimulus in copulation (aphrodisiac).

ORTHOPTERA

Blaberus craniifer (Burmeister), giant death's head roach

Virgin females produce a volatile sex pheromone which attracts males and elicits antennal waving, alertness, and locomotion toward the females (33). It is also interspecifically effective in releasing male courting behavior in *B. giganteus* and *Byrsotria fumigata*.

Blaberus giganteus (L.)

Virgin females may produce a volatile attractant for males, releasing courtship behavior (33).

Byrsotria fumigata Guérin, cockroach

Virgin females produce a volatile sex attractant which enables males to perceive them at a considerable distance and elicits alertness, antennal waving, and wing "pumping" (32, 33, 36, 280a). Females from which the corpora allata have been removed shortly after the imaginal moult fail to produce the attractant, but implantation of corpora allata causes recovery of this power. Allatec-

3

tomized females could be artificially coated with pheromone by rubbing them vigorously against a pheromone-producing female (280a).

Leucophaea maderae (F).

Smyth (315b) claims to have collected from females a volatile material which increases the incidence of courtship by males.

Mantis religiosa (L.), praying mantis

Caged virgin females can lure large numbers of males from a distance of up to 100 meters between 8:30 A.M. and 1 P.M. (199a).

Nauphoeta cinerea (Olivier), cockroach

The sex pheromone, if it exists, appears to be a nonvolatile substance on the female's surface. Male display (raising of the wings) is readily evoked, even by unreceptive females (33).

Periplaneta americana (L.), American cockroach

Females emit an odorous attractant for the male. The substance adheres to paper or other substances with which the females come in contact (281). Virgin females, as well as filter papers exposed to them, cause male alertness, antennal movement, searching locomotion, and vigorous wing flutter (33, 281). The wing-raising display, which is released much more readily in groups of males than in single males, is used as the single criterion of response in a bioassay method developed by Wharton et al. (349, 350). However, Jacobson and Beroza (186) have shown that a number of organic compounds, including several that are repellent to males, will elicit wing-raising, thus making it mandatory that an accurate bioassay show a combination of intense excitement, wing-raising, and attempts to copulate with one another.

The sex attractant is produced principally by virgin females and sporadically by mated females. Production is depressed drastically within eighteen hours after mating. A newly emerged female produces very little attractant; maximum production is attained by the second week. During the nonproductive phase, the female does not attract the male, and mating does not occur. Nymphs ordinarily do not produce the attractant. In females carbon-dioxide anesthetization and manual manipulation reduce the production of attractant somewhat. The attractant continues to be emitted during the course of normal oöthecal production, but a gradual decline occurs. Cathode-ray irradiation of 1000 and 2500 roentgens damages oöthecal and attractant production; with total inhibition of oöthecal production, females recover their capacity to produce the attractant and exceed the normal yield (351). Allatectomy of the female stops attractant production which resumes following implantation, usually into the abdomen, of a fresh corpus allatum (22). Cessation of attractant production by mating is triggered, at least partly, mechanically and is controlled through the nervous system.

The female sex pheromone is effective in releasing courting behavior in males of other *Periplaneta* species and in males of *Blatta orientalis*, but not in males of *Eurycotis floridana*, *Leucophaea maderae*, or *Nauphoeta cinerea* (33). The sex pheromones of other species of *Periplaneta* also appear to be interspecifically effective within the genus.

Periplaneta australasiae (Fabricius), **Australian cockroach**
Periplaneta brunnea (Burmeister)

Females of these two species produce pheromones that attract and sexually excite males. The same behavior is elicited by exposure of the males to filter papers over which females have walked (33).

Periplaneta fuliginosa (Serville)

Although virgin females appear to produce a chemical substance which acts as a releaser of courtship behavior in the male, the evidence for this is not yet conclusive (33).

LEPIDOPTERA

Achroea grisella (Fabricius), **lesser wax moth**
Achroea sp.

Adult virgin females elicit excitation in males of these species as well as those of *Galleria mellonella*; copulatory attempts have been made by the latter (28).

Acronicta psi (L.) (339)
Actias caja (L.), **garden tiger moth** (202)
Actias selene (Hübner)

According to Mell (235), marked males orientated toward the females from a distance of 11 km.

Actias villica (L.), **cream-spot tiger moth**

Females attract males at dusk. Countless male *Parasemia plantaginis* are also attracted by nearby *A. villica* females and attempt to copulate with them (200), leading Ford (127) to believe that the females of both species utilize the same sexual scent.

Agathymus baueri (Stallings & Turner)
Agathymus polingi (Skinner)

Observations made by Roever (276a) indicate that recognition of the males and females of both species for one another is bidirectional in that, while the initial recognition response is made by the male, the receptive female furthers this response by emitting a pheromone when the male approaches.

Aglia tau (**L.**), nailspot

The eighth abdominal segment of the adult female secretes an odorous substance that attracts the male for mating (106). This attraction could be demonstrated by laboratory tests using an olfactometer (300, 301).

Agrotis fimbria (**L.**) (339)

Agrotis ypsilon (**Hufnagel**), **black cutworm**

With the aid of a simple apparatus (125), it was determined that females at least one hour old produce an attractant for the males in their last two abdominal segments. The excised segments lose their attractiveness when placed in a vacuum, but they again become attractive within fifteen minutes (or two hours) after removal from the vacuum. The activity disappears completely from the cut segments after one and a half to three hours. The attractant may be collected from the abdominal segments with a stream of air ("freezing-out"), steam distillation, or extraction with various solvents, especially ether (123, 124).

Antheraea pernyi (**Guérin-Méneville**)

The presence of a sex attractant for this species was demonstrated by Schneider (293), using an electrophysiological technique.

Antheraea (*Telea*) *polyphemus* (**Cramer**), **polyphemus moth**

Rau and Rau (268) found that males marked on the wings with oil paint and released from the second or third story of a city building were able to return to virgin females without difficulty. Low temperature retarded the activity of these moths. Few or no males found the females unless they were liberated into the wind blowing from the direction of the females.

Aphomia gularis (**Zeller**)

Males exposed to females become highly excited, showing a typical circling dance. Although the female exhibits very small odor glands, those of the male (situated on the wings) are quite enlarged (28).

Argynnis adippe (**L.**) (339)

Argynnis euphrosyne (**L.**), **pearl-bordered fritillary** (339)

Argynnis latonia (**L.**) (339)

Argynnis paphia (**L.**), **emperor's cloak**

Females are highly attractive to males (339). According to Magnus (226), the male finds the female by sight, but once found she vigorously flaps her wings and slightly lifts the tip of her abdomen to release the odor which excites him.

The female attractant-producing glands consist of modified cells between the seventh and eighth abdominal rings. Drops of the liquid obtained from the sacculi laterales and placed on filter paper lure the males, which fan and distribute the attractant particles (167).

Autographa californica (Speyer), alfalfa looper

The sex pheromone was bioassayed by Gaston and Shorey (135a).

Bombyx mori (L.), silkworm moth

A newly emerged female placed in a container with males causes great excitement, and copulation occurs in a short time. A pupa containing a female soon to emerge is similarly attractive. Males and females may copulate immediately after emergence (227). Filter paper wetted with the liquid from the female's sacculi is highly attractive to a male when held close to his antenna (131).

The female protrudes a paired scent organ from the hindmost abdominal segment and the male walks nervously about, finds the female, and orients himself for copulation. The protruded female glands are withdrawn into the body immediately after being touched by a male. Excised scent glands, but not the mutilated female, are highly attractive and elicit copulatory attempts. Males will also mate with headless females (169, 199).

Extract of the female brought close to the male evokes vigorous wing flutter ("schwirrtanz") and attempts to locate the "female" (58).

A female assumes the calling position (protrusion of the scent organs) shortly after emergence; even mated females will assume this position. These females will then attract males, as will a piece of paper previously rubbed on the female's body. The effective distance of the attractant is 3–5 cm, although previously mated males will respond from a greater distance. Turpentine, eucalyptus, and clove oils do not attract males, but they do not detract from the female's attractiveness when placed near her. Males kept isolated from females may show sexual excitement, characterized by circus movements, rapid wing vibration, and bending of the abdominal extremity toward the head (81).

Males are attracted by unseen females or excised female abdomens. If the male's antennae are removed after he has been excited by the scent, he continues to search for the female but copulation occurs only if his abdomen touches her. Males can likewise be excited by air movement or by mechanical stimulation when crowded into a container without females. In the absence of air movement the male locates the female only with difficulty (308).

Cacoecia murinana (Hb.)

On a quadratic wooden frame (35 × 25 cm.), Franz (130) fastened a pane of wire glass covered with glue on both sides. In the center was placed a small cylindrical cage of 5-cm diameter whose front and rear walls consisted of nettle dust and whose side walls were provided with small openings to permit the scent of contained virgin females to escape. These traps were hung in June and July at the top, middle, or bottom of fir trees and attracted large numbers of males from the day of emergence to the eleventh day; no females were attracted to the traps. The largest number of males was attracted to cages hung near the treetop and the smallest number to those hung at the bottom. It was difficult to determine whether catches increased when increasing numbers of females were placed in a trap.

Caligula japonica (Butler) (339)

Callimorpha dominula (L.), scarlet tiger moth

The female is attractive to the male (202). Although the normal "calling time" for the female is from midnight to 5 or 6 P.M., a male was lured to a caged female at 11:15 P.M. (200). A female imprisoned in a muslin cage in the garden during daylight hours attracted male *Phragmatobia fuliginosa* (201). This led Ford (128) to assume that the scent produced by female *C. dominula* is the same as that produced by the female *P. fuliginosa*.

Callimorpha dominula persona (Hbn.)

Freshly emerged females of *C. dominula* and *C. dominula persona* can attract equal numbers of *C. dominula persona* males released nearby (258, 320, 339).

Callosamia promethea (Drury), promethea moth

A single female promethea moth, which has a strong odor perceptible to the human nose, attracted 40 males when placed near an open window. Low temperature retards the activity of these moths but they do not appear to be deterred by rain; large numbers of males have been observed to fly through heavy rain to reach a room in which females were confined. The attractive distance of a female varies from a few yards to a maximum of 3 miles (268).

Carpocapsa pomonella (L.), codling moth

Males can be lured into traps by using virgin females. Females that had been confined with males are also attractive to other males, but it is not shown that all the females have been inseminated. Trials with benzene or xylene extracts of female abdomens are inconclusive (264a).

Celaena haworthii (Curtis), Haworth's minor

Hordes of males seen flying excitedly around a tuft of grass in the evening were probably attracted by a female pupa about to hatch, according to Barrett (26).

Chaerocampa elpenor (L.)

Federley (121) reported several examples of cross-attraction and cross-mating between species of the sphingids. Male *C. elpenor* lured to field cages by their own females preferred to mate with *Metopsilus porcellus* females present in the same cages. In captivity, male *Deilephola galii*, *D. euphorbiae* and *Hyloicus pinastri* are attracted to and easily mated with female *C. elpenor*. However, in more cases than not, if a male *C. elpenor* mates with a female *M. porcellus*, he is unable to withdraw his penis and although the sperm has been introduced the mating is unsuccessful.

Clysia ambiguella (Hübner), grape berry moth

Experiments in the laboratory showed that two-day-old females excited males immediately, as shown by vibration of the male's wings and dancing around the females until copulation occurred. Such excitation occurred only in the evenings. Males placed in containers that had previously held a female became highly excited and made searching movements. *Clysia* females, whose odor is undetectable by humans, mate only once and thereafter are unattractive to males. *Clysia* females do not excite *Lobesia* (*Polychrosis*) *botrana* males, and vice versa (138).

Virgin females draw males in the field from at least 25 meters distant, the numbers drawn depending on the number and age of females and on the weather. Females one day old were more attractive than those two days old (139).

Colocasia coryli (L.) (339)

Colotois pennaria (L.) (202)

Cossus robiniae (Pck.)

One female lured 70 males within a few hours (307).

Cucullia argentea (Hufnagel), silver monk (339)

Cucullia verbasci (L.), *brown monk* (339)

Dasychira fascelina (L.)

Males are attracted to females in the field (339) and in a laboratory olfactometer (301).

Dasychira horsfieldi (Saund.)

Females contained in a glass jar covered with a thin sheet of writing paper attract no males until several pinholes are made in the paper, after which males begin to arrive quickly (147).

Dasychira pudibunda (L.), pale tussock moth

Females at emergence are attractive to males (107, 339). The attractant is an odorous material secreted by the eighth abdominal segment of the virgin adult female (106).

Dendrolimus pini (L.)

The adult females, which are capable of mating immediately upon emergence, possess special organs to lure the males (107).

Diatraea saccharalis (F.), sugarcane borer

Sticky traps baited with virgin females, their abdomens, or methylene chloride or benzene extracts of the abdomens can be used to attract and trap males in a cane field (257a). These females cease to be attractive after mating has occurred. The attractant is effective for only a few hours when exposed to the environment on filter papers.

Endromis versicolora (L.), Kentish morning glory (202)

Ephestia cautella (Walker), almond moth

A calling female 48 hours old placed in a container with a male *Plodia interpunctella* of the same age immediately evokes in the male all the symptoms of excitement (running in all directions, fluttering wings, vibrating antennae) usually manifest in response to the odor emitted by a calling female of its own species (95).

Ephestia elutella (Hübner), tobacco moth

Adults are ready for mating almost as soon as the wings are dry. Virgin females ready for mating begin "calling," sitting with their wings folded and the apical half of the abdomen bent over the back between the wings. Meanwhile the apical abdominal segments are alternately extended and retracted, exposing the intersegmental membranes. There is little doubt that during this process a scent attractive to the males is emitted. The segmental membranes, especially in the neighborhood of the orifice of the ductus bursae, have an appearance strongly suggesting the presence of secretory tissues. Males become very excited in the presence of these calling females (a pillbox from which a female had recently been removed had the same effect). The male begins fluttering around the female, who at first appears to take little notice or even runs away. Eventually she comes to a standstill and the male stands facing her, head to head, bending his abdomen. Almost immediately the pair twist around so as to be tail to tail. Females usually mate only once, sometimes twice, whereas males may mate repeatedly (273).

Male *E. kühniella* respond very strongly to females of this species and of *Plodia interpunctella* with a long-lasting characteristic dance and wing flutter (300). In olfactometer tests during which males were exposed to the air from virgin females, these males attempted to crawl through small openings to reach the females; when air free of lure was presented they showed no interest (301).

Females elicit excitation in males of this species, *E. elutella*, and *P. interpunctella* (28, 95). Such females also excite male *E. kühniella* and evoke copulatory attempts in these and *P. interpunctella* males (28).

Ephestia kühniella (Zeller), Mediterranean flour moth

A noncalling female placed in a glass-top container with males of *P. interpunctella* and *E. cautella* elicited mating attempts on the part of these males. Male *E. kühniella* whose eyes had been painted with India ink were placed in a container with a virgin female; the males became excited and one mated with her. Females 50 hours old were more attractive to males than newly emerged females. A male responded more rapidly to a female that had been calling for some time in a box prior to his entrance than to a female added to the box at the same time or slightly before his addition; this was probably due to the accumulation of the scent within the box (95, 273).

Eumeta crameri (Westw.)

Campbell (75) reported that a female placed in a closed tin box and put into his pocket attracted a male to his waist while walking in the field at dusk; the male hovered around Campbell's pocket. A muslin bag containing several females that was tied to branches in the garden attracted several dozen males.

Euproctis chryssorrhoea (L.), gold tail moth

Males respond excitedly in the laboratory to the presence of females (301).

The trapping method of Dyk (99) may be successfully utilized with males of this insect (213). A trap containing a single female lured 38 males in one day from a distance of 3 km. and 18 males on the second day (178).

Eupterotida fabia (Cram.)
Eupterotida undulata (Blanch.)

Males of both species were attracted to their respective females in Ceylon (147).

Galleria mellonella (L.), greater wax moth

Females elicit excitation in males of this species as well as of *Achroea grisella* and *Plodia interpunctella*; such excited *A. grisella* males will attempt to copulate with the female *G. mellonella* (28).

Grapholitha molesta (Busck), Oriental fruit moth

Females ready to mate attract the males and induce in them a mating response characterized by continuous vibration of the wings, a curving downward and forward of the abdomen, and short, darting runs or flights. The female ceases to be attractive once she has mated. Males may become so excited when near pairs attempting to mate that they lock their own genitalia firmly together (98a).

Harrisina brillians (B. & McD.), western grape leaf skeletonizer

Female moths were extracted with methyl anthranilate, a natural attractant occurring in grapes, and the extract was exposed in the field at 1.5 female equivalents per trap; three and a half times as many males were caught as females. Males were readily attracted in the field by a benzene extract of the virgin females. A concentration of 2 female equivalents in each of a variety of traps caught the following numbers of males: (*a*) metal tube (Graham) trap with screen ends but a cardboard Tanglefooted liner—19 males and no females; (*b*) type (*a*) trap with screened ends—14 males; (*c*) milk carton with inside walls Tanglefooted—3 males; (*d*) ice-cream carton with Kraft paper liner—13 males. A total of 77% of the males was caught during the first 24 hours, with the limit of attractiveness being about 36 hours. The benzene extract also attracted males to water-filled fiber-board pails hung on wires strung across stream beds along which grape vines were abundant (25).

Heliothis virescens (F.), tobacco budworm

Traps containing live virgin females, ether extracts of such females, or hexane extracts of the last two abdominal segments attracted and caught males in a greenhouse; equal numbers of males were caught by four and by eight female equivalents (135b). A bioassay apparatus for the pheromone was described by Gaston and Shorey (135a).

Heliothis zea (Boddie), bollworm, corn earworm, tomato fruitworm

The sex pheromone was bioassayed by the method of Gaston and Shorey (135a).

Heterusia cingala (Moore)

Males were attracted to females in Ceylon (147).

Hyalophora cecropia (L.), cecropia moth

The male cecropia moth is attracted to a female, flying upwind until he comes close to her, then he flutters in an aimless manner or directly toward her and mates immediately. Males released 5 feet from several excised female abdomens flew immediately to these abdomens, while dead or dying females as well as those from which the eggs had been removed were not attractive. Cocoons from which females had recently emerged were similarly unattractive. Although males prefer to go to virgin females, previously mated females are also attractive and males mate with them readily. Males make frantic efforts to mate with a female who is in the act of mating with another male. Females whose wings have been removed and replaced with wings from males remain attractive to males (232).

Boxed males unable to see caged females will fly to the females within 2 minutes after the entire ovipositor is protruded (317). Although females must be at least 16 hours old before they are capable of mating, partial protrusion of the ovipositor may occur at an earlier age. Once mated, a female is no longer attractive until her eggs have been laid.

Hyalophora colleta

Hyalophora euryalus (Boisduval), ceanothus silk moth

An electrophysiological method demonstrated that females of both species produce a sex attractant for their respective males (293).

Hypocrita jacobaeae (L.), cinnabar moth (339)

Hypogymna morio (L.) (339)

Laphygma frugiperda (J. E. Smith), fall armyworm

Extracts prepared from the caudal abdominal segments of virgin females elicit a mating response in unmated male moths. The response lasts from 1 to 3 minutes but can be reinduced after a rest period of 3 to 5 hours (307a).

Lasiocampa quercus (L.), oak eggar moth

Several males were attracted in the field to a bag that had contained a female a week before (155). A single female, of which the veteran naturalist, Fabre, had seen no specimen during twenty years of collecting in his locality, attracted 60 males (115). A box that had contained a virgin female 24 hours earlier attracted numbers of males in the field (23). Males were attracted to females in the laboratory (339).

A virgin female of this moth was besieged by larger numbers of male *Zygaena filipendulae* than by males of its own species; male *Z. trifolii* were not attracted (127, 328).

Kettlewell (203) reported that male *L. quercus* f. *callunae* released three-fourths of a mile downwind from a calling female easily reached her, whereas those released upwind required much longer to find the female.

Lasiocampa trifolii (Schiff.), grass eggar moth
Males are attracted to females in the field (202).

Lobesia (*Polychrosis*) *botrana* (Schiff.), grape vine moth
Males are attracted at least 20 to 25 meters by virgin females in the field (139). Virgin females squashed between the fingers also lure males (140).

Laboratory tests conducted with an olfactometer (shown in Figure 1) showed that males given a choice between 1 or 3 virgin females went directly to the 3 females (138). The olfactometer consisted of a glass tube 1-meter long and 2.5 cm in diameter, in the center of which, and at right angles to it, two short glass tubes branched off. To the shorter tube (6 cm) was attached a suction apparatus consisting of two bottles attached to one another by rubber tubing. One bottle was higher than the other; from it water flowed into the lower bottle so that air was drawn through the olfactometer into the upper chamber. Two empty glass flasks 12 cm long, which continued on one side into a glass tube 7 mm wide and 40 cm long, were drawn out on the right and left into the main tube.

Lymantria ampla (Walker)
Male moths flocked to a room in which a female had been kept, even after she had been mated and then killed several days before. Males continued to arrive for 10 to 14 days following her death, fluttering around the breeding cage in which she had been confined (147).

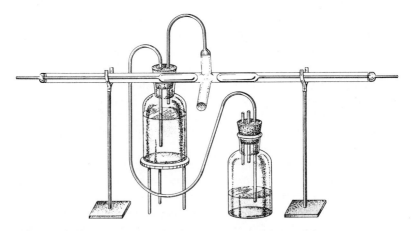

Figure 1. Laboratory olfactometer used to bioassay the sex attractant of the grape vine moth. [Redrawn from B. Götz, *Z. angew. Entomol.*, **26**, 143 (1939), Verlag Paul Parey, Berlin.]

Mahasena graminivora (Hampson), bagworm

The female bagworm, following complete development, pushes the tip of her abdomen slightly out of the pupal case and emits a strong characteristic odor which pervades the surrounding air. The male flies about seeking the female; after settling on the pupal case, he inserts his abdomen between the wall of the case and the ventral surface of the female to achieve mating (309).

Malacosoma neustria (L.), lackey moth

The female attracts the male by odor (13, 99).

Metopsilus porcellus (L.)

See *Chaerocampa elpenor* (page 9).

Micropteryx spp.

Unpaired males of species of *Micropteryx* often pay more attention to a copulating pair than to solitary females (272).

Orgyia antiqua (L.), vapourer moth, rusty tussock moth

The larvalike female with her threadlike antennae sits on her pupal case and is sought out by the males (301).

A newly emerged female held in a gauze-covered container lures numerous males during a period of 2 to 3 hours. The attractant-producing gland is located in the female abdomen. Minute drops of liquid may be seen on the surface of the everted glands. If this liquid is absorbed on blotting paper and held before a fresh male, he behaves exactly as if he were in a female's presence, fluttering his wings and attempting to copulate with the paper (131).

Orgyia ericae (Germ.)

The dorsal odor glands of the female are very highly developed. The female does not leave the pupal case, merely extending the tip of her abdomen through an opening in the sac to await arrival of the male (339).

Orgyia gonostigma (Fabricius) (339)

Parasemia plantaginis (L.), wood tiger moth

Females attract males during daylight hours (200, 203), whereas *Actias villica* assemble at dusk (200). However, countless male *P. plantaginis* attracted by females of this species will attempt to mate with *A. villica* females nearby. Female *P. plantaginis* also attract male *A. villica* (200). This led Ford (128) to assume that the females of both species produce the same attractant.

Pectinophora gossypiella (Saunders), pink bollworm moth

Flaschenträger, et al. (125) reported that a chemical sex attractant for male pink bollworm moths is produced by the females.

Before mating, the male moths exhibit a state of excitation

(premating dance) including rapid wing vibrations, with intermittent curving of the abdomen upward while stationary or crawling. Males are attracted to a mating pair and begin the premating dance; a pair crushed during copulation is especially attractive to males. Specimens of both sexes 1 to 6 days old were placed in cages, and pairs that mated were collected in a jar containing methylene chloride and stored at 45°F. The pairs were then homogenized with mortar and pestle, the extract was filtered, and the solvent was removed at 100 to 120°F. with the aid of a stream of air. Filter paper was impregnated with an aliquot of oily extract diluted with methylene chloride and placed in small cup-type traps hung in wire screen cages (24 × 32 × 24 in.) containing free-flying males. A gentle stream of air was found to be essential to obtain positive responses from the males (preliminary trials showed that only males were attracted into these traps when placed among a mixed population). The tests were conducted during daylight hours (although it could be shown that twice as many males could be caught in complete darkness), using the equivalent of 9 to 11 mating pairs in each trap. The attractant extract remained highly effective on the lure retainer for at least 32 days at approximately 85°F. (251, 252). The terminal 2 to 3 segments of the abdomens of 4- to 5-day-old females were later found to be the best source of the sex attractant—a crude methylene chloride extract of such segments eliciting a positive response from males when tested at one-fiftieth of a female equivalent per milliliter. Active extracts were obtained from all females, regardless of time of day collected, with methylene chloride, acetone, benzene, chloroform, ethanol, or methanol. Males readily responded with their characteristic dance to the vapors expelled from a glass pipette contaminated with the attractant. Males used in bioassays were aged for 4 to 5 days under continuous light, since they did not respond as readily during daylight hours if the lights were turned off at night (38).

Phalera bucephala (**L.**), moonspot

The odor of an unmated female enclosed in a room will attract males, but it is not detectable to humans (339).

Plodia interpunctella (**Hübner**), Indian meal moth

Virgin females ready for mating begin "calling" and soon are surrounded by highly excited males (273). Males introduced into boxes from which calling females have just been removed begin to flutter their wings violently and behave as though they are in pursuit of a female. Males never become sexually excited in the presence of a noncalling female. It is highly probable that the assumption of the calling position, by stretching the intersegmental membrane of the ventral body wall, exposes the mouths of the glands so that the scent is emitted. It is also possible that the glands are under nervous control. Calling on the part of the female is not continuous; it is characterized by an abdomen bent dorsally so that it projects between the wings (250). Males show immediate excitement when placed in a dish that had contained a female for 3 or 5 minutes, fleeting or weak excitement in a dish exposed to a female for 1 minute, and no response when placed in a dish exposed to a female for 0.5 minute. The following effects are shown by males introduced into a dish at various times after it has contained a female for 5 minutes: 1 or 2 minutes, great excitement; 5 minutes, weak excitement; 10 minutes, excitement of very short duration; 20 minutes or longer, no response (223).

Males respond to the females with a long-lasting characteristic dance and wing fluttering; whirring of a few seconds' duration is sometimes caused by a sudden jarring or exposure to light. After whirring for 40 seconds to several minutes, short resting pauses are observed before beginning again. Males introduced into petri dishes that have contained a female always show a characteristic response, even though as long as 66 minutes may have elapsed since removal of the female (300).

A male of this species introduced into a container of females of three *Ephestia* species immediately shows all the symptoms of sexual excitement (running in all directions, fluttering wings, vibrating antennae) and makes repeated attempts to mate (95). Although Barth (28) had reported that males of *Ephestia* species do not respond sexually to female *P. interpunctella*, Schwinck (300) showed that these females did evoke strong sexual excitement in male *E. kühniella*. When males and females of both species are placed in a container, males follow females of the other species and attempt to mate, but anatomical differences prevent copulation. Laboratory bioassay tests were conducted in an olfactometer shown in Figure 2 (300).

Porthesia similis (Fuessly) (339)
Porthetria (Lymantria) dispar (L.), gypsy moth

Male gypsy moths are attracted to the females by scent (126, 205, 206). Urbahn (339) reported that 17 males flew excitedly into a room adjoining his garden, and followed by other males, they went directly to a pupal rearing box. Careful searching located a newly emerged female in a corner of the box, not readily apparent from outside the box.

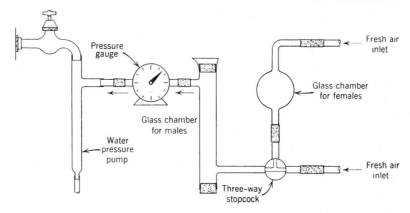

Figure 2. Laboratory olfactometer for the bioassay of sex attractants of various lepidopterous insects. [Redrawn from I. Schwink, Z. *vergl. Physiol.*, **35**, 167 (1953), Springer Verlag, Berlin.]

The female does not fly, but the male is a strong flier. The male proceeds to find the female by following the scent through zigzag flight, usually against the wind carrying the scent (82). Schedl (287) states that the females cannot fly prior to laying their eggs but then are able to fly for a short distance.

Jacentkovski (178) placed virgin female gypsy moths in traps located in infested woods (177), checking them twice a day for male catches. Of numerous males caught in these traps, the majority were trapped during daylight hours, mainly about noon. The effective distance of the lure was about 100 meters. Empty containers that had previously held females remained attractive to males for 2 to 3 days.

Sexually excited males show a whirling dance, moving the wings first with small then with large amplitude and then attempting to copulate with the females; these dances are quite different from flight movements. Excited females also show whirling, probably to create air movement in order to disperse the lure. Males marked with oil paints and released from four directions nearly all flew into the wind (301).

A laboratory bioassay method for testing substances for attractiveness involved exposure of filter paper (squares or rolled cartridges), glass rods, or vials previously in contact with the substance to males held captive by their wings to plastic, spring-type clothespin mounts hung from pins on a wooden rack. Tests were conducted in still air, but air was circulated in the laboratory between tests. An active substance elicited flicking movements of both antennae and curvature of the abdomen in the direction of the test object. Laboratory results appeared to be in general agreement with field data on the attractiveness of various compounds and extracts (44, 45).

Porthetria dispar japonica (Motsch), gypsy moth

Olfactometer tests (300) with this insect as well as with *P. dispar* showed definite chemical attraction of the female for the male (301).

Porthetria (Lymantria) monacha (L.), nun moth

The female, which emerges from the pupal case ready to mate and containing ripe eggs, possesses special organs to lure the male (107). A single live female placed in a trap lured males in an infested area (7). Although Komareck (213), Jacentkovski (177), and Ambros (10) reported that a female ceases to be attractive upon oviposition, Nolte stated to Komareck (213) that he could not substantiate this and believed it to be true only if the female had first been fertilized by the male. Glass vials containing a female with a piece of cotton wool were kept until oviposition occurred; the female was then removed and the vial stoppered and made air-tight with lacquer. Such vials could be used at least a year later to trap males (99).

Prodenia litura (Fabricius), Egyptian cotton leaf worm

The female attracts the male with an odor that appears one hour after emergence (123, 124) but is produced in highest yield when the insect is 1 to 2 days old (156).

Prodenia ornithogalli (Guenée), yellow-striped armyworm

The sex pheromone was bioassayed by Gaston and Shorey (135a).

Protoparce sexta (Johannson), tobacco hornworm

Virgin female moths placed in gauze-covered cages can lure males, and mating sometimes occurs through the cloth. All males arrive after midnight and most matings occur between midnight and 1 A.M. Males may be close to virgin females and yet pay no attention to them. The female does not appear to be attractive to the male until she drops her abdomen (calling); mating occurs a short time afterward (8).

An active extract can be obtained with ethyl ether, benzene, or acetone but not with ethyl alcohol. Filter papers wetted with the active extract were placed in small cages exposed to free-flying males in a large walk-in cage; attraction was shown by the small cage being visited by males between 10:30 P.M. and 3 A.M. Alcohol extracts found to be inactive had been tested on filter paper, sponges, or cotton lamp wicks. So-called attractive females chosen for clipping were determined by exposing them in the small cages suspended from the roof of the large cage (9).

Pterostoma palpina (L.), snout spinner (339)
Ptilophora plumigera (Schiff.) (202)
Pygaera curtula (L.) (339)
Pygaera pigra (Hufn.) (339)
Rhyacionia buoliana (Schiff.), pine shoot moth

When approaching a receptive female the male beats his wings rapidly and curls the tip of his abdomen upward, opening and closing his claspers. A single virgin female may attract numerous males to the tree on which she is resting. A scent released by the female probably attracts the male. First moth activity occurs at about 5 P.M., with peak flight intensity at 7:30 to 8:30 P.M.; the activity decreases to zero by 9:30 P.M. A virgin female confined in a small cylindrical cage of nylon net and plastic hung from a tree attracted 31 males in 10 minutes, whereas an ovipositing female attracted 7, and a mated female none (260).

Rhyacionia frustrana (Comstock), Nantucket pine tip moth

A total of 24 plywood traps similar to those used by Coppel (83) were baited with virgin females, the boards were coated with Tanglefoot, and the traps were suspended about 5 feet above the ground in a stand of loblolly pine at 15-foot intervals; traps were arranged randomly in two rows. Males were attracted to these traps, even to those in which mixed sexes had been placed. Unmated females were not attractive after death. Virgin females were most attractive early in their life span, becoming unattractive with age; they remained attractive up to 9 days. No females were caught in any trap during the 10-day exposure period, while a total of 200 males was trapped (357).

Rothschildia orizaba (Westwood), orizaba silkmoth

Electrophysiological bioassay showed the female to be attractive to the male (293).

Samia cynthia (Drury), cynthia moth (268)
Sanninoidea exitiosa (Say), peach tree borer

Females are ready to mate about an hour after emergence, raising the tip of the abdomen in the characteristic "calling" position to emit the odor which attracts males to them (315a).

Saturnia carpini (Schiff.)

Forel (129) reported that several females placed in a window in Lausanne brought a swarm of males.

Saturnia pavonia (L.), emperor moth, peacock moth

A newly emerged female attracted from a distance 127 males between 10:30 A.M. and 5 P.M. (320). A newly emerged female lured 40 males in an evening and numerous others on 8 additional evenings (115). The female, which possesses scent sacs, remains inactive all night and until forenoon, then begins "calling" until evening; males fly mainly during the forenoon and early afternoon (339).

Saturnia pavonia minor (L.), lesser peacock moth

A female may attract numerous males (23). Many males visited a captive female between noon and 2 P.M. (117). However, two males with their antennae removed could not locate a female they had previously found with ease (98).

Saturnia pyri (L.)

A female attracts numerous males (339). A newly emerged female held captive in a wire cage in Fabre's home attracted, in the hours before midnight, numerous males through an open window of another room (116).

Smerinthus ocellatus (L.), eyed hawk moth

A single virgin female in a muslin cage hung outside a window attracted 42 males in 8 days (346).

Solenobia fumosella (Hein.)

Males of this species immediately begin to flutter if a newly emerged "calling" female S. triquetrella is brought into their vicinity, but copulation does not occur. However, if the male is first excited by a female of his own species and, at the last moment, a female S. triquetrella is substituted underneath him, copulation is successful (305).

Solenobia lichenella (L.)
Solenobia seileri (Sauter)
Solenobia triquetrella (Hbn.)

The members of these three species are parthenogenetic and can be crossed specifically. Females do not leave the pupal sac but protrude their abdomens from it and mating occurs with attracted males. Introduction of a pupal case with a "calling" female into a container holding a resting male causes the male to begin fluttering; he flies to her, the ovipositor is withdrawn into the sac. and mating follows (306).

Sphinx ligustri (L.), privet hawk moth

Males of many hawk moths are able to detect the virgin females from incredible distances (244).

Female S. ligustri attract male Smerinthus ocellatus and copulation may be effected (258).

Spilosoma lutea (Hufn.), buff ermine moth

Female *S. lutea* held captive in a wire net insectary in a garden attracted male *Actias caja* in the morning (105).

Spodoptera exigua (Hübner), beet armyworm

The sex pheromone was bioassayed by Gaston and Shorey (135a).

Stilpnotia salicis (L.), satin moth

Males are attracted and excited by virgin females (301).

Synanthedon pictipes (Grote & Robinson), lesser peach tree borer

The female is highly attractive to the male (136a). Manual squeezing of the virgin female's abdomen causes the protrusion of the terminal three segments, which are highly attractive to males. These segments are normally protruded to their utmost when the females are "calling," at which time the segments will attract males from as far away as 500 feet. Excised abdomens remain attractive for about 20 minutes (81a).

Tineola bisselliella (Hummel), webbing clothes moth

Males attracted to "calling" females by odor move about actively, vibrating their wings. Antennae-less males cannot perceive the odor. Mating occurs in the morning or afternoon, in either bright light or shadow (332). The sexually excited male walks about rapidly with his abdomen extended, vibrating or fluttering his wings continuously. This behavior may be observed as soon as 4 hours after emergence. Females observed in the "calling" pose protrude and retract the ovipositor and vibrate its tip. Excised abdomens, but not the heads and thoraxes, of 1-day-old females were attractive to males; a few males made genital connection with the severed abdomens. Males are often attracted to copulating pairs of moths. One female abdomen will activate a male from a distance of 1.5 cm, whereas ten severed abdomens will activate from 7 cm. Males do not respond to male abdomens, but they may court in the presence of other males (282).

Trabala vishnu (Lef.)

A newly emerged female will attract large numbers of males (147).

Trichoplusia ni (Hübner), cabbage looper

Females attractive to males in screened laboratory cages between midnight and 4 A.M. were immediately collected and the terminal two or three abdominal segments were extracted with methylene chloride. The extract of one female on a filter paper strip caused receptive males to move their antennae 90 degrees from a position along the anterior margin of the forewing to an elevated position in a wide vee along the head, followed at once by rapid wing vibration, slight elevation of the abdomen, and eventual flight to the source of the stimulus. Males repeatedly tried to mate with the strips and with nearby males, but not with un-treated strips. Cylindrical ice-cream carton traps (8-cm diameter, 23-cm long), with screen funnel ends, containing extract-treated strips were placed in a screened cage (60 × 80 × 60 cm) containing 50 virgin males 4 days old; a 6-cm fan provided air circulation in the cage. The trap caught 5 males within 15 minutes, whereas a check (empty) trap caught none. About 99% of 7 to 8-day-old males held under continuous light responded within 2 to 3 minutes to one-twentieth female equivalent by rapid wing vibration and antennal excitation; the duration of response was 2 to 5 minutes. Males 17 to 18 days old could still respond to a female, but the largest numbers of males responded at 3 to 4 days of age (173).

The sex pheromone of the cabbage looper is bioassayed at 1 to 5 A.M. in diffuse light by noting the number of males that start to vibrate their wings or fly after exposure to an ethyl-ether extract of the female abdominal tips. The original bioassay proce-dure could be used to detect a concentration as low as that equiva-lent to 1×10^{-4} female, but pheromone contamination of the labora-tory air caused variable results. Subsequent development of a bioassay apparatus utilizing a completely closed flow system and an external air source resulted in a quantitative method sensitive to the 10^{-6} female equivalent level (135a). The sensitivity of this type of bioassay depends on the effort taken to exclude males from ex-traneous contact with the pheromone (313a, 313c). The sex pheromone is produced in glands in the terminal abdominal seg-ments and released when the female assumes a typical receptive posture. The male antennae form the principal site for perception of the pheromone. Behavioral experimentation failed to show that the male produces an attractant or excitant for the female, despite a previous report (313) that adults of either sex assume an "attrac-tive attitude" for the opposite sex, remaining stationary with the wings spread out horizontally or fanning (314).

Vanessa urticae (L.) (339)

Zygaena filipendulae (L.), six-spot burnet moth

A female *Lasiocampa quercus* moth was besieged by swarms of male *Z. filipendulae;* she seemed more attractive to them than did female *Z. filipendulae* (328). This led Ford (127) to state "there can be little doubt that the female *L. quercus* produces the same scent as *Z. filipendulae.*"

COLEOPTERA

In his extensive review of female and male scent glands, Richards (272) quotes Lengerken to the effect that the degenerate female of drilid beetles is very attractive to the males, which can be "assembled" just as in the saturniid moths. The male has large branched antennae, whereas those of the female are simple in structure. Numerous species of beetles in which the male possesses large antennae use these organs to find the female.

Evers (114) reported that the elytral and cranial organs of male Malachiidae, a family of tiny beetles usually found in the tropics, are involved in male and female love play, and Matthes (21, 231) found that the females attract the males during the mating season.

Agriotes ferrugineipennis (LeConte), click beetle
Ctenicera destructor (Brown), click beetle
Ctenicera sylvatica (Van Dyke), click beetle

Females of each of these species are attractive to their respective males. The attractant can be extracted from the abdomens of such females with ether or 70% ethanol. The attractants are species-specific (225a). Doane (95a) was the first to suggest the presence of a sex attractant in *C. destructor* when he reported that caged females attracted males in the field.

Diabrotica balteata (LeConte), banded cucumber beetle

A sex attractant produced by females by the time they are 10 days old lures males in the field from as far as 40 feet. Males responding to the lure rise from the plants in which they are resting and approach upwind in a characteristic hovering flight. When air movement is gentle and steady, they locate the source with little difficulty. When a gusty wind is blowing, they frequently lose the scent and wander off in the wrong direction. Unmated females remain attractive to males for as long as 70 days. Most females cease to be attractive after one mating and none are attractive after two matings. The attractant may be extracted from the female abdomens with ethyl alcohol; extracts of heads and thoraxes and of filter papers on which females have crawled give negative results. Under ideal conditions, a 10-female equivalent of the abdominal extract will elicit a response from males up to 49 feet from the lure, but few respond at this distance. At temperatures below 65°F., both sexes are inactive and there is little response. No consistent, recognizable response from males caged indoors has been detected (84).

Dytiscus marginalis (L.)

Blunck is reported by Hesse and Doflein (169) to have found that females are highly attractive to males.

Hemicrepidius morio (LeConte)

Screen cages containing Douglas-fir bark or logs, placed on the ground in the field, attracted large numbers of this species, 99% of which were males. Although the evidence would not permit a definite conclusion to be drawn with certainty, Chapman (79) theorized that females had emerged in these cages and were releasing an attractant for the males.

Hylecoetus dermestoides (L.)

The male detects the female from a distance by means of his maxillary palpae, which are well supplied with nerve stalks (136).

Limonius californicus (Mann.), sugar-beet wireworm

Males are attracted in large numbers to newly emerged females (310). The female releases a sex attractant for the male soon after her emergence. An extract prepared from two dead virgin females with 70% ethyl alcohol caused male excitation, but an extract of fertilized females did not elicit this response. Microscope slides moistened with the active extract attracted numerous males upwind in an infested field within 10 seconds from as far away as 40 feet. The males moved rapidly toward the slides, crawling and flying excitedly over the slides and repeatedly extruding their genitalia. In laboratory tests, a positive response was obtained with a female abdominal extract but not with an extract of the heads and thoraxes (225). As little as 0.4% of the ether extract of a single female abdomen frequently elicited a maximum sexual response from males in a laboratory olfactometer (225a).

Limonius sp., wireworm

Traps containing females attracted males in enormous numbers soon after emergence, but the catches dropped off as soon as numerous wild females appeared (219).

Melolontha vulgaris (Fabricius) (161)

Pachypus cornutus (Olivier)

Females of these beetles are wingless and produce a sex attractant that brings males to them (191a).

Phyllophaga lanceolata (Say), June beetle

Mating begins about daylight, when the adults emerge from the ground. Although males may feed on the same leaf with a female, as soon as she extrudes her genitalia, males within a radius of 15 to 20 yards fly toward her. Exposure of a smashed female initiated male flight; females did not respond to a "calling" female. A female crushed and thrown on the ground when the sun was obscured by a cloud attracted only a few nearby males, but when the sun reappeared numerous males became active and flew toward the injured female. In the absence of a breeze, males from all sides from a distance of 15 to 20 feet flew toward the point of origin of the attractant; in a breeze, only male beetles within 3 to 10 feet were attracted from the windward side, whereas those on the leeward side were attracted from a distance of 30 to 40 feet (333).

Rhopaea magnicornis (Blackburn)

Large numbers of males were observed trying to dig their way into a field cage containing a virgin female. Cups previously used to house 4- to 15-day-old virgin females elicited in males a graded response of fanning out the lamellae of the antennal club and excited walking, culminating in rapid fluttering of the wings and searching behavior. Laboratory females produced the attractant from the third day of adult life and were no longer attractive to males following fertilization. The attractant is emitted from the abdomen, no other portion of the female's body being attractive to males. Field tests with marked males conducted during the insect's active period of 1 to 2 hours after sundown showed that caged females were attractive to males up to 30 yards away; recoveries of marked males were greatly dependent on wind speed, since males flew at random in unsteady or very low winds but flew upwind to females in steady breezes of 5 to 7 miles per hour (316a).

Rhopaea morbillosa (Blackburn)
Rhopaea verreauxi (Blanchard)

Caged virgin females of these species are capable of emitting their respective attractants on at least three successive nights and, presumably, until a successful mating is achieved. However, in Nature, mating probably takes place soon after a female begins producing the attractant (316a).

Telephorus rufa (L.)

Two males excited by the same female inserted their penis into the female at the same time (169).

Tenebrio molitor (L.), yellow mealworm

Shaking a live female in a vial releases a strong odor that lures and excites males. A glass rod, paper, or cotton pressed to a female abdomen becomes wet with a yellow liquid; holding these treated objects in front of and above a male's head makes him highly excited so that he attempts to copulate with the objects, which he can be made to follow. This may be used as a bioassay for the attractant. The odor itself does not seem to be that of the lure, as both males and females release it when agitated. Material obtained from the male abdomen does not excite females or other males, but a male may be made attractive to other males by rubbing the tips of his elytra with the squeezed posterior end of a female's abdomen (340).

HYMENOPTERA

Apis mellifera (L.), honey bee

A honey bee swarm ordinarily contains from 5000 to more than 50,000 workers, zero to several thousand drones, and a single queen (Figure 3). Such swarms are part of the reproductive process. The source of the odorous substances responsible for a swarm's detection of its queen appears to be glands in her head, as grinding these heads with a mortar and pestle and placing them on filter paper causes workers to cluster round and to chew the paper (241). The queen's mandibular glands are also suggested as a possible source of an odor attracting drones to virgin queens for mating (271).

A virgin queen attracts males when she reaches a height of 12 meters from the ground; the males are attracted first by her movement and then by her odor (285, 369). Drone honey bees are not attracted to queens below approximately 15 feet above the ground, and drone swarms attracted to tethered queens at greater heights disperse quickly if the queens are lowered too near the ground. Drones swarmed in large numbers around queens tethered at a height of 30 to 80 feet within 100 yards of an apiary. Squashed virgin queens on filter papers tested in this way are very attractive, whereas untreated control papers attract only an occasional drone. Although the primary source of the attractant appears to be a pair of mandibular glands in the queen's head, as shown by testing extracts of various portions of her body, extirpation of these glands does not necessarily render a virgin queen incapable of mating. Supplementary stimuli such as vision may be utilized by drones to locate virgin queens in flight (135, 242). Silicic acid

Figure 3. Swarm orientation of honey bees. Queen is confined in a container held by the researcher. [From R. A. Morse, *Science*, **141** (3578), 357 (1963), American Association for the Advancement of Science, Washington.]

fractionation of an ethereal extract of virgin queen mandibular glands indicates that "queen substance" (9-oxo-*trans*-2-decenoic acid) and a phospholipid fraction are responsible for the attraction, but reconstitution of the gland lipid fractions into the lipid complex considerably increases the attraction for drones (135).

Pain and Ruttner (254) were able to verify Gary's results (135). They reported that queen substance does not attract workers, inhibit ovaries, or cause construction of combs, but it does inhibit queen cell formation. A virgin queen was tethered around the thorax with a 50-cm length of nylon string attached to a plastic balloon (1.30 meters high and 60 cm in diameter) that was regulated from the ground by a 15-meter length of nylon cord. Tests were conducted in August during the hours of 1 and 3 P.M. Queens attracted males when suspended 6 to 15 meters from the ground; those showing signs of fatigue were replaced by fresh queens. Queen substance and an ethereal extract of the queen mandibular glands were each impregnated on plastic forms resembling queens, and these were compared with live queens for attractiveness. A fertile queen attracted and maintained a swarm of males, as did old virgin queens, while a control attracted 1 to 2 males for a short period. A swarm of males was attracted and maintained by mandibular extract or by 1.14 mg of its acidic fraction, but not by an ovarian extract from three virgin females. A fertile queen appeared to attract and maintain a swarm more rapidly than did a virgin queen.

Although queen substance had been tentatively identified as the substance responsible for the stabilization of honey bee swarms by queens (71, 134, 253, 316), this phenomenon is due to the action of 9-hydroxy-*trans*-2-decenoic acid (72).

An odor gland (Nassanoff gland) situated in the abdominal end of various races (*carnica, ligustica,* and *nigra*) of *A. mellifera* protrudes when the bee wishes to attract companions. The pleasant odor, which attracts all races, is dispersed by the simultaneous fanning of the wings. The colony odor, which adheres to the bodies, distinguishes companions of their own colony from foreigners (270). The odor appears to be caused by a mixture of geraniol, nerolic acid, and possibly geranic acid (46, 47, 48).

Bracon hebetor (Say) (=*Habrobracon juglandis*), wasp

Males of this insect, a parasite of *Ephestia* larvae, run about excitedly flapping their wings when introduced to females (148, 352). The presence of a camel's hair brush recently used for handling females also excited males (148). No courtship takes place, the excited male mounting as soon as he has located the female. Stimulation is apparently by odor perceived largely by the antenna (246). Some females fail to excite males. Males may mate with a single female more than once but are essentially excited by the introduction of new females and will mate with several in succession (352). Filter papers on which females have been crushed evoke an immediate mating response from males. Several female abdomens elicited attempts by males to copulate, some of which were successful; the anterior half of the abdomen was more attractive than the posterior half (149).

Male *Habrobracon brevicornis* introduced to females of *B. hebetor* are greatly stimulated, attempting to mount and mate with them. The female may refuse to mate, but sometimes mates immediately afterward with a male of her own species (352).

Crabro cribrarius (L.), wasp

An odorous sex attractant for the male is produced by the female's abdomen. Although the active substance was not isolated, dummies rubbed mechanically with freshly caught females attracted males that attempted copulation with these dummies (214, 215).

Dasymutilla spp., velvet ants

Females placed in small cages were very attractive to males (120, 172).

Diprion similis (Hartig), introduced pine sawfly

Virgin females in the field attract exceptionally large numbers of males; one caged female lured more than 11,000 males within 5 days. Males can be attracted approximately 200 feet out of the forest over an open field. Benzene extracts of crushed females or their abdomens and ethyl ether rinses of glassware in which the females had crawled were highly attractive (83). Copulation results in a rapid loss in attractancy; mating appears to trigger a mechanism that allows destruction of the attractant in the female. A satisfactory laboratory bioassay for the attractant has not as yet been developed (77).

Gorytes campestris (L.), wasp

An odorous sex attractant for the male is produced by the female's abdomen (214, 215).

Gorytes mystaceus (L.)

Females are highly attractive to males (215, 216).

Macrocentrus ancylivora (Rohwer)

Males introduced into a glass vial previously occupied by a female become excited and behave in the same manner as when in the presence of a female. Copulation usually takes place soon after emergence (122).

Macrocentrus gifuensis (Ashmead)

Sexual activity of males is more pronounced when they are not confined in a small space, where the air may become saturated with the female odor. Males respond sexually immediately after emergence (256).

Macropis labiata (Fabricius)

Females are highly attractive to males in the field (215).

Megarhyssa atrata (Fabricius)

Males of this species, a parasite of wood-boring insects, emerge before females. They are attracted by a female scent, congregating at the point from which the females will emerge. A single individual of a group of 6 to 10 males on a dead tree was found to have his abdomen inserted through an opening in the wood; cutting into the wood revealed that the male was mating with a female inside (78).

Megarhyssa inquisitor (Say)

A number of males of this species, predatory on *Malacosoma neustria*, were observed trying to enter into a few openings in a *Malacosoma* pupa. It was found that several female *M. inquisitor* were inside and the males were lured by the female scent (345).

Megarhyssa lunator (L.)

Males congregate on the trunk of a tree awaiting the emergence of females, which are certainly detected by odor (1, 2). The males are often observed to be scraping away the bark to a depth of 0.25 inch to find females ready to emerge. Copulation takes place while the female is still in her cell or burrow, after which she flies off to oviposit (132).

Neodiprion lecontei (Fitch), red-headed pine sawfly

Virgin females attract large numbers of males (37a).

Neodiprion pratti pratti (Dyar), Virginia-pine sawfly

Males are strongly attracted to a virgin female, approaching her with their wings spread upward and outward and the antennae expanded. Live females as well as extracts of their abdominal segments lure males to field cages from a distance of 50 to 100 feet. Females mate only once, becoming unattractive to males within less than a minute after copulation. Although males were strongly attracted during 1960 and a high percentage mated, females were not attractive to males in 1963 and only 2.5% mated. No explanation was found for this loss in attractiveness (45a).

Praon palitans (Muesebeck)

A male is ready to mate soon after emergence. He detects the virgin female by odor, becoming highly excited and running about with his wings held vertically above the thorax and with his antennae vibrating rapidly. Once contact is made, the male moves his wings rapidly in a vertical position. Once mated, the female loses her attractiveness for males, unless they come in contact with her accidentally (289).

Pristiphora conjugata (Dahlb.), sawfly

A male that had just finished copulating was introduced into a vessel containing only males. He immediately became the subject of much attention from his companions, who attempted to mate with him (89).

DIPTERA

Among the Psychodid males, a male that has just mated with a female is very attractive to other males, who attempt to copulate with him (272).

Culiseta inornata (Williston), mosquito

Males exposed to an extract of virgin females show increased sexual activity characterized by excited flight, searching, and copulatory attempts with other males (211).

Drosophila melanogaster (Meigen)

According to Spieth (319), Sturtevant found that pairs of this species could be induced to copulate much more readily if the glass vial in which they were placed had just previously been occupied by another pair of courting individuals. Apparently the courting actions of the first pair resulted in the release of a substance into the vial that served as a stimulus to the second pair. Several days elapse before a mated female is receptive to another male (166).

Musca domestica (L.), house fly

Tests with an olfactometer and with simulated, treated fly models ("pseudo-flies") gave evidence that females produce one or more volatile chemical substances which can elicit mating behavior patterns in males. The pheromone is soluble in benzene and is species-specific; extracts of *M. autumnalis* (face fly) or *Stomoxys calcitrans* (stable fly) females do not affect the behavior of male *M. domestica*. The pheromone is present in the heads, thoraxes, and abdomens of mature females, in their eggs, and in minor amount in males (277, 278).

Phytophaga destructor (Say), hessian fly

Females in small field cages attract large numbers of males upwind from a distance of 10 to 15 feet (76).

ISOPTERA

Reticulitermes arenincola (Goellner), termite
Reticulitermes flavipes (Kollar), eastern subterranean termite

Following flight, females of both species attract males by odor. When the male touches the female, she lowers her abdomen and is followed in tandem. Males also follow the severed tip of the female abdomen, or other males if once attracted by the female. The odor is detected by the male's antennae (110).

Table 1 lists those insect species in which females have been shown to lure the males.

TABLE 1.   INSECTS IN WHICH FEMALES LURE THE MALES

Order	Scientific Name	Common Name	References
Orthoptera	*Blaberus craniifer* (Burmeister)	Giant death's head roach	33
	Blaberus giganteus (L.)		33
	Byrsotria fumigata (Guérin)	Cockroach	32, 34
	Leucophaea maderae (F.)	Cockroach	315b
	Mantis religiosa (L.)	Praying mantis	199a
	Nauphoeta cinerea (Olivier)	Cockroach	33, 280
	Periplaneta americana (L.)	American cockroach	281
	Periplaneta australasiae (Fabricius)	Australian cockroach	33
	Periplaneta brunnea (Burmeister)		33
	Periplaneta fuliginosa (Serville)		33
Lepidoptera	*Achroea grisella* (Fabricius)	Lesser wax moth	28
	Achroea sp.		28
	Acronicta psi (L.)		339
	Actias caja (L.)	Garden tiger moth	202
	Actias selene (Hübner)		235
	Actias villica (L.)	Cream-spot tiger moth	200
	Agathymus baueri (Stallings & Turner)		276a
	Agathymus polingi (Skinner)		276a
	Aglia tau (L.)	Nailspot	106, 301
	Agrotis fimbria (L.)		339
	Agrotis ypsilon (Hufnagel)	Black cutworm	123, 124
	Antheraea pernyi (Guérin-Méneville)		293
	Antheraea (Telea) polyphemus (Cramer)	Polyphemus moth	268
	Aphomia gularis (Zeller)		28
	Argynnis adippe (L.)		339
	Argynnis euphrosyne (L.)	Pearl-bordered fritillary	339
	Argynnis latonia (L.)		339
	Argynnis paphia (L.)	Emperor's cloak	226, 339

TABLE 1 *(Continued)*

Order	Scientific Name	Common Name	References
Lepidopetra	*Autographa californica*		
(Contd.)	(Speyer)	Alfalfa looper	135a
	Bombyx mori (L.)	Silkworm moth	131, 169, 339
	Cacoecia murinana (Hb.)		130
	Caligula japonica (Butler)		339
	Callimorpha dominula (L.)	Scarlet tiger moth	200, 201, 202
	Callimorpha dominula per-sona (Hbn.)		258
	Callosamia promethea (Drury)	Promethea moth	268
	Carpocapsa pomonella (L.)	Codling moth	264a
	Celaena haworthii (Curtis)	Haworth's minor	26
	Chaerocampa elpenor (L.)		121
	Clysia ambiguella (Hübner)	Grape berry moth	138, 139
	Colocasia coryli (L.)		339
	Colotois pennaria (L.)		202
	Cossus robiniae (Pck.)		307
	Cucullia argentea (Hufnagel)	Silver monk	339
	Cucullia verbasci (L.)	Brown monk	339
	Dasychira fascelina (L.)		339
	Dasychira horsfieldi (Saund.)		147
	Dasychira pudibunda (L.)	Pale tussock moth	106, 107, 339
	Dendrolimus pini (L.)		107
	Diatraea saccharalis (F.)	Sugarcane borer	257a
	Endromis versicolora (L.)	Kentish glory moth	202
	Ephestia cautella (Walker)	Almond moth	95
	Ephestia elutella (Hübner)	Tobacco moth	28, 95
	Ephestia kühniella (Zeller)	Mediterranean flour moth	95, 273
	Eumeta crameri (Westw.)		75
	Euproctis chrysorrhoea (L.)	Gold tail moth	178, 213
	Eupterotida fabia (Cram.)		147
	Eupterotida undulata (Blanch.)		147
	Galleria mellonella (L.)	Greater wax moth	28
	Grapholitha molesta (Busck)	Oriental fruit moth	98a
	Harrisina brillians (B. & McD.)	Western grape leaf skeletonizer	25
	Heliothis virescens (F.)	Tobacco budworm	135b

TABLE 1 (*Continued*)

Order	Scientific Name	Common Name	References
Lepidoptera (*Contd.,*)	*Heliothis zea* (Boddie)	Bollworm, corn earworm, tomato fruitworm	135a
	Heterusia cingala (Moore)		147
	Hyalophora cecropia (L.)	Cecropia moth	317
	Hyalophora colleta[1]		293
	Hyalophora euryalus (Boisduval)	Ceanothus silk moth	293
	Hypocrita jacobaeae (L.)	Cinnabar moth	339
	Hypogymna morio (L.)		339
	Laphygma frugiperda (J. E. Smith)	Fall armyworm	307a
	Lasiocampa quercus (L.)	Oak eggar moth	23, 115, 155
	Lasiocampa trifolii (Schiff.)	Grass eggar moth	202
	Lobesia (*Polychrosis*) *botrana* (Schiff.)		138, 139
	Lymantria ampla (Walker)		147
	Mahasena graminivora (Hampson)	Bagworm	309
	Malacosoma neustria (L.)	Lackey moth	13, 99
	Metopsilus porcellus (L.)		121
	Micropteryx spp.		272
	Orgyia antiqua (L.)	Vapourer moth, rusty tussock moth	131
	Orgyia ericae (Germ.)		339
	Orgyia gonostigma (Fabricius)		339
	Parasemia plantaginis (L.)	Wood tiger moth	200, 203
	Pectinophora gossypiella (Saunders)	Pink bollworm moth	125, 251
	Phalera bucephala (L.)	Moonspot	339
	Plodia interpunctella (Hübner)	Indian meal moth	250, 273
	Porthesia similis (Fuessly)		339
	Porthetria (*Lymantria*) *dispar* (L.)	Gypsy moth	126, 205, 206
	Porthetria dispar japonica (Motsch)	Gypsy moth	301
	Porthetria (*Lymantria*) *monacha* (L.)	Nun moth	107

[1] An authority name could not be located for this insect.

TABLE 1 (*Continued*)

Order	Scientific Name	Common Name	References
Lepidoptera (*Contd.*)	*Prodenia litura* (Fabricius)	Egyptian cotton leaf worm	123, 124
	Prodenia ornithogalli (Guenée)	Yellow-striped armyworm	135a
	Protoparce sexta (Johannson)	Tobacco horn-worm	8, 9
	Pterostoma palpina (L.)	Snout spinner	339
	Ptilophora plumigera (Schiff.)		202
	Pygaera curtula (L.)		339
	Pygaera pigra (Hufn.)		339
	Rhyacionia buoliana (Schiff.)	Pine shoot moth	260
	Rhyacionia frustrana (Comstock)	Nantucket pine tip moth	357
	Rothschildia orizaba (Westwood)	Orizaba silk moth	293
	Samia cynthia (Drury)	Cynthia moth	268
	Sanninoidea exitiosa (Say)	Peach tree borer	315a
	Saturnia carpini (Schiff.)		129
	Saturnia pavonia (L.)	Emperor moth, peacock moth	115, 320
	Saturnia pavonia minor (L.)	Lesser peacock moth	23, 117
	Saturnia pyri (L.)		116, 339
	Smerinthus ocellatus (L.)	Eyed hawk moth	346
	Solenobia fumosella (Hein.)		305
	Solenobia lichenella (L.)		306
	Solenobia seileri (Sauter)		306
	Solenobia triquetrella (Hbn.)		306
	Sphinx ligustri (L.)	Privet hawk moth	244
	Spilosoma lutea (Hufn.)	Buff ermine moth	105
	Spodoptera exigua (Hübner)	Beet armyworm	135a
	Stilpnotia salicis (L.)	Satin moth	301
	Synanthedon pictipes (Grote & Robinson)	Lesser peach tree borer	81a, 136a
	Tineola biselliella (Hummel)	Webbing clothes moth	282, 332
	Trabala vishnu (Lef.)		147
	Trichoplusia ni (Hübner)	Cabbage looper	173

TABLE 1 *(Continued)*

Order	Scientific Name	Common Name	References
Lepidoptera	*Vanessa urticae* (L.)		339
(Contd.)	*Zygaena filipendulae* (L.)	Six-spot burnet moth	127
Coleoptera	*Agriotes ferrugineipennis* (LeConte)	Click beetle	225a
	Ctenicera destructor (Brown)	Click beetle	95a, 225a
	Ctenicera sylvatica (Van Dyke)	Click beetle	225a
	Diabrotica balteata (LeConte)	Banded cucumber beetle	84
	Dytiscus marginalis (L.)		169
	Hemicrepidius morio (LeConte)		79
	Hylecoetus dermestoides (L.)		136
	Limonius californicus (Mann.)	Sugar-beet wire-worm	225, 310
	Limonius sp.	Wireworm	219
	Melolontha vulgaris (Fabricius)		161
	Pachypus cornutus (Olivier)		191a
	Phyllophaga lanceolata (Say)	June beetle	333
	Rhopaea magnicornis (Blackburn)		316a
	Rhopaea morbillosa (Blackburn)		316a
	Rhopaea verreauxi (Blanchard)		316a
	Telephorus rufa (L.)		169
	Tenebrio molitor (L.)	Yellow mealworm	340
Hymenoptera	*Apis mellifera* (L.)	Honey bee	135
	Bracon hebetor (Say) (= *Habrobracon juglandis*)	Wasp	246, 352
	Crabro cribrarius (L.)	Wasp	214, 215
	Dasymutilla spp.	Velvet ant	120, 172
	Diprion similis (Hartig)	Introduced pine sawfly	83
	Gorytes campestris (L.)	Wasp	214, 215

TABLE 1 *(Continued)*

Order	Scientific Name	Common Name	References
Hymenoptera	*Gorytes mystaceus* (L.)		215, 216
(Contd.)	*Macrocentrus ancylivora*		
	(Rohwer)		122
	Macrocentrus gifuensis		
	(Ashmead)		256
	Macropis labiata (Fabricius)		215
	Megarhyssa atrata		
	(Fabricius)		78
	Megarhyssa inquisitor (Say)		345
	Megarhyssa lunator (L.)		1, 2
	Neodiprion lecontei (Fitch)	Red-headed pine sawfly	37a
	Neodiprion pratti pratti (Dyar)	Virginia-pine sawfly	45a
	Praon palitans (Muesebeck)		289
	Pristiphora conjugata		
	(Dahlb.)	Sawfly	89
Diptera	*Culiseta inornata* (Williston)	Mosquito	211
	Drosophila melanogaster		
	(Meigen)		319
	Musca domestica (L.)	House fly	277, 278
	Phytophaga destructor (Say)	Hessian fly	76
Isoptera	*Reticulitermes arenincola*		
	(Coellner)	Termite	110
	Reticulitermes flavipes (Kollar)	Eastern subterranean termite	110

CHAPTER THREE

OCCURRENCE AND DEMONSTRATION OF SEX ATTRACTANTS (OR EXCITANTS) IN THE MALE

ORTHOPTERA

Byrsotria fumigata (Guérin), cockroach

A pheromone produced by the courting male causes the female to straddle the male's abdomen and begin feeding on his tergum (280a, 282a).

Eurycotis floridana (Walker)

The male produces a pheromone, even when not actually courting, that attracts the female (33).

Leucophaea maderae (F.), cockroach

The male produces a pheromone that attracts the female (315b).

HEMIPTERA

Lethocerus indicus (Lepetier & Serville), giant water bug

During sexual excitement the male is easily recognized by its odor, for its abdominal glands secrete a liquid with an odor reminiscent of cinnamon (69, 73). This substance, produced in two white tubules 4 cm long and 2–3 mm thick, occurs to the extent of approximately 0.02 ml[4] per male and is used in southeast Asia as a spice for greasy foods. The female does not secrete the sub-

39

stance, which is believed to act as an aphrodisiac to make her more receptive to the male.

Rhoecocoris sulciventris (Stal.), bronze orange bug

A substance obtained from both sexes of this insect may act as an attractant or aphrodisiac (255).

LEPIDOPTERA

Much has been written, particularly in the older literature, about the odor glands of male moths and butterflies, describing their anatomy and physiology. A review of the subject (85) appearing in 1885 extends back to the seventeenth century. In 1878, Müller (243) described the occurrence of an odor, perceptible to humans and probably serving to lure or excite the female, in males of 44 species of butterflies. The odoriferous organs are usually located on the wings, but sometimes they occur on the hind legs or abdomens.

Acherontia atropos (L.)

The male abdomen contains odor organs important in sexual behavior (174).

Achroea grisella (Fabricius), lesser wax moth

The male attracts and excites the female. A total of 25 males placed in a gauze-covered beaker set in the corner of a large rectangular dish (93 cm long, 70 cm wide, 14 cm high) lured 25 virgin females from the opposite corner. An attempt to lure males with virgin females was unsuccessful. A female placed in a cage with a male immediately approached him as she began to flutter and copulation followed shortly (217).

Aphomia gularis (Zeller)

Wing glands in the male secrete an odorous substance attractive to the female (27).

Argynnis adippe (L.)
Argynnis aglaja (L.)
Argynnis paphia (L.), emperor's cloak

Sex organs situated on the wings of males of these three species secrete odorous substances which excite the female sexually (29, 226).

Caligo arisbe (Hbn.)

Glandular lamina of the fourth and fifth abdominal segments in males produce an odor which is initially pleasantly aromatic but later becomes rancid. This odor probably serves to excite the female sexually (30).

Colias edusa (Fabricius)

Wing scales of the male release an odorous substance which is sexually exciting to the female (174).

Danaus plexippus (L.), monarch butterfly

Males possess odor glands on the wing folds and at the abdominal tips. The odorous substance probably serves to excite the female sexually (174).

Elymnias undularis (Dru.)

Males emit a vanilla odor which excites the females just before mating (153).

Ephestia cautella (Walker), almond moth

Males bend their abdomen in a dorsal direction similar to the female "calling" position; this exposes scent glands which produce an odor sexually exciting to females. Absence of these scent tufts in the male may prevent copulation (95).

Ephestia elutella (Hübner), tobacco moth

Wing glands of the male secrete an odorous substance that increases the female's excitement in copulation. Vibration of the wings disperses the odor (27).

Erynnis tages (L.)

Scent glands on the costal margins of the male's wings release an aphrodisiac for females (174).

Eumenis semele (L.)

Special scent organs of the male are displayed to the female by means of a peculiar bowing movement; the odor evokes the mating attitude in the female (330).

Euploea phaenareta (Schall)

Males emit a vanilla odor which excites the females just before mating (153).

Euploea sp.

The male abdominal tips and wing scales contain glands that emit an odor sexually exciting to females (174).

Eurytides protesilaus (L.)

Hairy scent glands, pierced by a single canal, on the male's wings secrete an odorous substance that may act as an aphrodisiac for females (346).

Galleria mellonella (L.), greater wax moth

Wing glands in the male secrete an odorous substance highly attractive to the female (30). The male vibrates his wings and dances around, thus dispersing the attractive odor that brings the female to him with vibrating wings. The musklike odor may be released from the undersides of the front wings 12 hours after the male emerges; the female approaches with a circling dance, fanning her wings rapidly and undulating her abdomen (344). Although Röller, et al. (279) detected the odor in males about 2 to 24 hours old, it was not musklike; it was at its maximum during evening hours. The male behavior was not influenced by allatectomy, gonadectomy, or both, or by implantations of additional corpora allata in the pupae or in adults.

Hepialus behrensi (Stretch.)

Glands on the leg of the male emit a scent attractive to females (275).

Hepialus hectus (L.)

Glands on the tibia of the male emit a scent attractive to females (88, 275). The scent was described as being pineapplelike by Deegener (87), who also studied the anatomy and physiology of the glands.

Hipparchia semele (L.), grayling butterfly

The male is provided with scent scales on his wings. At the climax of courtship, he clasps the female's antennae between his wings, bringing them in contact with the scent scales and causing the female to become receptive to his advances (331).

Lethe rohria (F.)

Males emit an odor that excites the females just before mating (153).

Lycaena spp.

The male has scent glands scattered over his wings that release an odor sexually exciting to females (174).

Mycalesis suaveolens (W. M. & N.)

Males emit an odor that excites the females just before mating (153).

Opsiphanes invirae isagoras (Fruhst.)

Males possess glandular lamina on the fourth and fifth abdominal segments that secrete a volatile material with a vanillinlike odor which may serve to excite the female before or during mating. It can be extracted from the glands with chloroform. The odor can be detected by humans after the material has stood for about 2 weeks at 25–35°; it becomes weak after 3 weeks, and is no longer detectable after 4 weeks. Crystals found in the secretion probably do not contain the odorous material, as they can still be seen after the odor is no longer detectable (30).

Otosema odorata (L.)

The hind legs of the male possess a honeylike odor which may serve to excite the female sexually (31).

Panlymnas chrysippus (**L.**)

Males possess odor glands on the wing folds. The odorous substance produced by these glands probably serves to excite the female sexually (174).

Papilio aristolochiae (**F.**)

The male emits an odor to excite the female just before mating (153).

Pechipogon barbalis (**Cl.**)

Glands situated on the tibia and femur of the male secrete a substance that excites the female sexually (174).

Phassus schamyl (**Chr.**)

Males possess odor glands on the tibia which secrete a substance attractive to females (88).

Phlogophora meticulosa (**L.**), angleshade moth

The male produces a substance sexually attractive to the female (128).

Pieris napi (**L.**), mustard white
Pieris rapae (**L.**), imported cabbageworm

In these species glands scattered on the male's wings secrete an odorous substance which is sexually attractive to their females (174, 346).

Plodia interpunctella (**Hübner**), Indian meal moth

A male attracted to a female by her odor dances around her vibrating his wings (28). In so doing he releases and disperses from his wing glands an odorous substance which serves to increase the female's excitement during copulation (27). Females placed in a dish previously occupied for 5 minutes by a sexually excited male immediately moved about excitedly, waving their antennae and assuming a "calling" position (223).

Sphinx ligustri (**L.**)

Scent glands at the base of the male's abdomen secrete an aphrodisiac for the female (174).

Stichophthalma camadeva (**Westw.**)

Males emit an odor that excites the female just before mating (153).

Syrichtus malvae (**L.**)

The costal margins of the male's wings contain scent glands that produce an aphrodisiac for the female (174).

Terias hecabe fimbriata (**Wall.**)

The male's wing scales contain glands that emit an odor sexually exciting to females (174).

Tineola biselliella (**Hummel**), webbing clothes moth

Males attracted by females move about excitedly, vibrating their wings. This probably serves to distribute the male's odor, exciting the female sexually (332).

Xylophasia monoglypha (**Hufn.**), dark arch moth

The male produces a substance sexually attractive to the female (128).

COLEOPTERA

Males of Malachiidae, a family of tiny tropical beetles, entice females first with a tarty nectar and then expose them to an aphrodisiac. The males possess tufts of fine hair growing out of their shells (in some species on the wing covers, in others on the head). These hairs are saturated with a glandular secretion that the females cannot resist. During the mating season, the male searches for a female; when he finds one he offers his tuft of hair, which the female then accepts and nibbles upon. In so doing, her antennae come in contact with microscopic pores in his shell, through which the aphrodisiac substance is excreted, thus putting her in a state of wild excitement (21, 231).

Anthonomus grandis (**Boheman**), boll weevil

A substance produced by males attracts females from distances of 2 to 30 feet. Air drawn continuously over males in a cage was passed through charcoal, which was then extracted with chloroform; removal of solvent from the extract gave a substance with a musty, faintly minty odor. Females responded quickly to this substance by rapid walking, standing high on their front legs, and holding their antennae high and forward. Females were caught in traps baited with the chloroform extract (198).

HYMENOPTERA

Bombus terrestris (**L.**), bumble bee

According to Richards (272), Sladen suggested in 1912 that male bumble bees emit a scent for attracting the females to places visited by the males. The male often has a sweet fragrance not detectable in the females. The males have a curious habit of flying in procession from place to place, the spots visited usually being the hollows at the bases of trees. Male *B. terrestris* swarm in the summer by releasing an odorous material which brings the females to them for mating. The attractant, which can be extracted from the male heads (mandibular glands) with pentane, has been identified as farnesol; it is not found in body extracts of males or workers, and occurs in worker heads in only trace amounts. Farnesol is present in the flower oils of many plants, and it is possible that the males take up farnesol with their food and feed it into their mandibular glands (324, 325).

DIPTERA

Ceratitis capitata (Wied.), Mediterranean fruit fly

Mature virgin females are attracted over a short distance and sexually excited by a volatile chemical substance emanating from the erectile anal ampoules of sexually mature males (121a,b). The substance is dispersed by air currents set up by the vibrating wings of males. Immature and fertilized females do not respond to the attractant.

Drosophila melanogaster (Meigen)

According to Spieth, cited by Mayr (233a), the wing flutter shown by males before mating probably serves to throw an air stream toward the courted female. This air, containing the male's scent, stimulates the female and increases her receptivity.

Drosophila victoria (Sturtevant)

Males produce an attractant (or aphrodisiac) for the females. Virgin females deprived of their antennae fail to accept males' overtures owing to their failure to receive olfactory stimuli; despite this, males attempt to copulate with them (319).

MECOPTERA

Harpobittacus australis (Klug), scorpion fly
Harpobittacus nigriceps (Selys), scorpion fly

Males of both species hunt for the soft-bodied insects on which they feed; females have never been observed hunting, capturing, or killing prey in the field. When the male holds its prey and begins to feed, two reddish-brown vesicles are everted on the abdomen between tergites 6–7 and 7–8 and begin to expand and contract, discharging a musty scent perceptible to humans. This scent attracts females to the vicinity of the male, moving upwind in his direction. As soon as the female is within reach, the male retracts his vesicles and brings the prey to his mouthparts. The female attempts to get hold of the prey but is prevented by the male, whose abdomen seeks out the tip of the female's abdomen and copulation takes place. Once in copula, the male voluntarily passes the prey with his hind legs over to the female (51).

NEUROPTERA

Osmylus chrysops (L.)

The apex of the male's abdomen is swollen and the eighth tergite is enlarged and rounded, containing extrudible white scent glands. On the second day after emergence, as twilight sets in, he crawls to a position in which he can hang down freely and display his abdomen. The glands extrude to their full extent and he thus spends the night, unless a female is near. Almost immediately, females within a foot or two become agitated and wave their antennae vigorously. Female and male walk toward one another and courtship takes place, followed by mating. The male rarely flies and is less active than the female (355).

Table 2 lists those insect species in which males have been shown to lure or excite the females.

TABLE 2.   INSECTS IN WHICH MALES LURE OR EXCITE THE FEMALES.

Order	Scientific Name	Common Name	References
Orthoptera	*Byrsotria fumigata* (Guérin)	Cockroach	280a, 282a
	Eurycotis floridana (Walker)		33
	Leucophaea maderae (F.)	Cockroach	315b
Hemiptera	*Lethocerus indicus* (Lepetier & Serville) (= *Belostoma indica*)	Giant water bug	73
	Rhoecocoris sulciventris (Stal.)	Bronze orange bug	255
Lepidoptera	*Acherontia atropos* (L.)		174
	Achroea grisella (Fabricius)	Lesser wax moth	217
	Aphomia gularis (Zeller)		27
	Argynnis adippe (L.)		29, 226
	Argynnis aglaja (L.)		29, 226
	Argynnis paphia (L.)	Emperor's cloak	29, 226
	Caligo arisbe (Hbn.)		30
	Colias edusa (Fabricius)		174
	Danaus plexippus (L.)	Monarch butterfly	174
	Elymnias undularis (Dru.)		153
	Ephestia cautella (Walker)	Almond moth	95
	Ephestia elutella (Hübner)	Tobacco moth	27

TABLE 2 (*Continued*)

Order	Scientific Name	Common Name	References
	Erynnis tages (L.)		174
	Eumenis semele (L.)		330
	Euploea phaenareta (Schall.)		153
	Euploea sp.		174
	Eurytides protesilaus (L.)		346
	Galleria mellonella (L.)	Greater wax moth	30, 344
	Hepialus behrensi (Stretch.)		275
	Hepialus hectus (L.)		87, 88, 275
	Hipparchia semele (L.)	Grayling butterfly	331
	Lethe rohria (F.)		153
	Lycaena spp.		174
	Mycalesis suaveolens (W.-M. & N.)		153
	Opsiphanes invirae isagoras (Fruhst.)		30
	Otosema odorata (L.)		31
	Panlymnas chrysippus (L.)		174
	Papilio aristolochiae (F.)		153
	Pechipogon barbalis (Cl.)		174
	Phassus schamyl (Chr.)		88
	Phlogophora meticulosa (L.)	Angleshade moth	128
	Pieris napi (L.)	Mustard white	174
	Pieris rapae (L.)	Imported cabbage worm	174, 346
	Plodia interpunctella (Hübner)	Indian meal moth	22, 223
	Sphinx ligustri (L.)	Privet hawk moth	174
	Stichophthalma camadeva (Westw.)		153
	Syrichtus malvae (L.)		174
	Terias hecabe fimbriata (Wall.)		174
	Tineola biselliella (Hummel)	Webbing clothes moth	332
	Xylophasia monoglypha (Hufn.)	Dark arch moth	128
Coleoptera	*Anthonomus grandis* (Boheman)	Boll weevil	198
		Malachiidae beetles	21, 231

TABLE 2 (*Continued*)

Order	Scientific Name	Common Name	References
Hymenoptera	*Bombus terrestris* (L.)	Bumble bee	272
Diptera	*Ceratitis capitata* (Wied.)	Mediterranean fruit fly	121a,b
	Drosophila melanogaster (Meigen)		233a
	Drosophila victoria (Sturtevant)		319
Mecoptera	*Harpobittacus australis* (Klug)	Scorpion fly	51
	Harpobittacus nigriceps (Selys)	Scorpion fly	51
Neuroptera	*Osmylus chrysops* (L.)		355

CHAPTER FOUR

ATTRACTANTS PRODUCED BY ONE SEX TO LURE BOTH SEXES (ASSEMBLING SCENTS)

The following insect species in the order Coleoptera are treated separately in this presentation because one sex produces a substance, under special circumstances, which causes both sexes to assemble for mating.

Dendroctonus brevicomis (LeConte)

Dendroctonus frontalis (Zimm.)

Dendroctonus pseudotsuga (Hopkins)

Sexually mature, unmated females of these species feeding on fresh Douglas fir phloem produce a volatile substance to which both males and females of the respective species respond in flight; no response is obtained to males, excised mated females, or sexually immature females. Although the attractant may be produced over a long period of time, production is terminated once mating occurs. Three log sections were each provided with 40 female beetles, and the resulting frass and excrement was collected in distilled water. The attractive substance contained in the boring dust and excrement was washed out with petroleum ether; the resulting extract, placed in field olfactometers arranged in a circle of 5-yard radius, attracted beetles released from the center (284, 340a, 341a). *D. frontalis* also responded to an attractant collected from *Pinus ponderosa* that had been infested with *D. brevicomis* (341a).

49

Males and females of *Gnathotrichus sulcatus* and *G. retusus* also respond to the borings produced by female *D. pseudotsuga* and to alcohol extracts of such borings (284b). In the absence of material freshly infested by their own species, *Ips avulsus, I. calligraphus,* and *I. grandicollis* respond to logs infested with *D. frontalis* (341a).

Ips avulsus (Eichh.)
Ips calligraphus (Germ.)
Ips confusus (LeConte)
Ips grandicollis (Eichh.)
Ips ponderosae (Sw.)

A volatile substance responsible for mass attraction of both males and females of *I. confusus* and *I. ponderosae* is obtained from the hindgut of mature males of the respective species and from their frass, and by condensing the air drawn from a box containing beetle-infested ponderosa pine logs (340a, 341, 356, 356a). The attractant is released only after emerging males have fed for several hours on new host material and the gut has been filled. Trees and logs that have been fed upon may retain their attractiveness for approximately 10 days following infestation, but lose their activity with loss of moisture. Feces and frass pushed out of the entrance hole by males are also attractive, but neither feeding females nor their frass will cause assembling. Materials were tested in laboratory olfactometers, flight bars, a flight mill, a flight arena, cages, and field olfactometers. Response of both sexes to the attractant occurs immediately, indicating that flight exercise is not a prerequisite to response in this species (133, 210, 341). In olfactometer tests, *Ips avulsus, I. calligraphus,* and *I. grandicollis* were attracted in large numbers by volatile materials emanating from log sections of southern pines recently infested by the respective species. Of all the species investigated, *I. grandicollis* responded least specifically (341a).

Microscopic examination showed the ileum of mature males to consist of enlarged cells with large nuclei. The histological findings were consistent with previous olfactory tests implicating the hindgut of mature males as well as their fecal matter as the source of the species-specific pheromone. One hypothesis proposes a holocrine-type secretion of the pheromone into the gut lumen, where it becomes attached to the fecal matter; its release therefore depends on defecation which depends, in turn, on the successful invasion of new host material. This phenomenon may be interpreted as an efficient survival mechanism, since it guides the population in flight only toward breeding material that proved suitable (259).

Lycus loripes (Chevrolet)

A volatile attractant produced by the males causes both males and females to aggregate, and then distribute themselves into individual mating pairs or small clusters of pairs (108).

Trypodendron lineatum (Oliv.), ambrosia beetle

Fertilized and unmated females boring into the wood of *Pseudotsuga menziesii* produce a volatile substance to which both males and females respond in flight. No response is obtained to either males or virgin females feeding on the wood. An alcohol extract of the frass from feeding, fertilized females is similarly attractive to both sexes. No other species is attracted (284a,b).

CHAPTER FIVE

ANATOMY AND PHYSIOLOGY
OF THE PRODUCTION GLANDS

A good review of the literature pertaining to the scent glands of male and female insects was given by Richards (272), in 1927, who stated "scent organs are found to be of very wide and, in many groups, fragmental occurrence in insects, playing an essential part in mating. When they occur in the female alone their function is to bring the sexes together, while those peculiar to the males are used, in nearly all cases, to rouse the female to the state in which she is ready to copulate."

By far the greatest amount of work on the function of the production glands has been conducted with the Lepidoptera. Urbahn (339) published a comprehensive treatise in 1913 on the abdominal scent organs of female butterflies. These organs, in *Phalera bucephala*, consist, in their simplest form, merely of a saddle-shaped field in the last intersegmental membrane between the eighth and ninth abdominal segments. When stretching the abdomen, the intersegmental fold is simultaneously stretched to the outside. Deep ring-shaped scent glands are present in the noctuids *Cucullia verbasci* and *C. argentea*. Dorsally situated scent glands of the last intersegmental fold are present in *Hypogymna morio* and *Dasychira pudibunda*. Scent sacs are formed either singly or in pairs on each side of the body; they are situated either dorsally or ventrally and are withdrawn by means of special muscles. Such scent sacs are found in *Bombyx mori*, *Argynnis paphia*, *Saturnia pavonia*,

52

and *Brenthis euphrosyne*. The "glandulae oliferae" originate by the transformation of the last intersegmental fold to a pair of glandular hoses which extend deep into the cavity of the eighth abdominal segment on both sides of the body. These hoses are found in *Vanessa urticae*, *Acronicta psi*, and *Argynnis paphia*. The dorsal odor glands of female *Orgyia ericae* are very highly developed and the female does not leave the pupal case, merely extending the abdominal tips through an opening in the case to await the male's arrival.

Urbahn (339) also studied carefully and described at length (80 pages) the abdominal scent glands of female *Hypocrita jacobaeae*, *Callimorpha dominula*, *Caligula japonica*, *Aglia tau*, *Argynnis latonia*, *A. adippe*, *A. euphrosyne*, *Agrotis fimbria*, *Pterostoma palpina*, *Colocasia coryli*, *Porthesia similis*, *Dasychira fascelina*, and *Orgyia gonostigma*.

Freiling (131) described in considerable detail the male and female odor organs of numerous Lepidoptera. A detailed discussion of the release of sex odors (and other odors, as well) by Lepidoptera is that of Hering (167). The excised female glands lure males that attempt to copulate with these glands, no heed being paid to the mutilated female. The female glands are usually modified cells between the eighth and ninth abdominal segments, although in *Argynnis* species they occur between the seventh and eighth rings. Drops of the liquid obtained from the "sacculi laterales" placed on filter paper lure males that attempt to copulate with the paper. The hairs on the underside of the female abdomen serve to fan and distribute the attractant particles.

Virgin, sexually mature females of *Ephestia* and *Plodia* commence "calling" by sitting with the wings folded and the apical half of the abdomen bent over the back between them. Meanwhile the apical abdominal segments are alternately extended and retracted, so that the intersegmental membranes are widely exposed. There is little doubt that during this process a scent attractive to the males is emitted. The segmental membranes, especially in the neighborhood of the orifice of the ductus bursae, have an appearance strongly suggesting the presence of secretory tissues (273).

Eltringham (109) has described scent glands and brushlike organs in male *Xylophasia monoglypha* and *Phlogophora meticulosa*. These are situated in a long narrow pocket in the abdominal cuticle, starting in the first segment and running along either side for about 6 mm. It is slitlike, with the edges pressed closely together. Inside it is housed a brush which can be opened, like a fan, by muscle fibers. This is composed of very numerous, long, narrow scales up each of which penetrates a minute tube from a gland cell at its base. It is evidently a distributing organ for the stimulating scent, presumably used when flying in proximity to a female.

A detailed study was made of the sexual scent organs of male and female *Ephestia kühniella, E. cautella, E. elutella,* and *Plodia interpunctella* by Dickins (95). In the males, scent scales are situated dorsally on the eighth abdominal segment. In the female *E. cautella,* the organs show gland cells and are much more complex than those in *E. kühniella* or *P. interpunctella;* the organs are present on the last (ninth) abdominal segment. *E. cautella* shows typical "glandulae odoriferae," not shown by any of the other species.

Barth (28) found that the head, thorax, wings, and the front half of the abdomen of female *Plodia interpunctella* did not evoke a courting dance in males, whereas the abdominal tips (segments 7–9) did evoke such a response, except with males whose antennae had been removed. Microscopic examination of the segments showed no odor scales or odor hairs, but two glands from part of the hypodermis of the intersegmental membrane were easily seen between segments 8 and 9. Tension of the cuticula and a resulting increase in blood pressure causes the secretion to be evolved.

Male *Plodia interpunctella* never become excited in the presence of noncalling females. It is highly probable that the assumption of the calling position, with resultant stretching of the intersegmental membrane of the ventral body wall, exposes the mouths of the glands so that the scent is emitted. It is also possible that the glands are under nervous control (250). Calling by the virgin female is not continuous. Very rarely females failed to call, and dissection of these and of females with males that would not pair, although they were calling, showed no gross abnormalities. Müller (245) also postulated that, in the case of *P. interpunctella,* the female ready for copulation stretches the ninth abdominal segment vertically upward, eventually stretching the last intersegmental membrane to expose the scent glands.

Hammad and Jarczyk (156) found the scent organs of the female Egyptian cotton leafworm (*Prodenia litura*) in the last abdominal segments. Histologically, these organs are tufts of modified scales or hairs with gland cells at their base, covering the ninth abdominal segment. During the resting period this segment is invaginated into the eighth segment. Large droplets of oil-like secretion cover more than one cell and at the same time penetrate the overlying cuticle. No special secretory ducts are found in the glandular epithelial cells. The hairs have the function of increasing the evaporating surface of the secretion. There is no similarity in form or position between the sexual scent organs of *P. litura* and those described by Götz (145) for other noctuids.

The attractive substance in the lesser peach tree borer (*Synanthedon pictipes*) is located somewhere on the terminal three segments of the female abdomen. Females are attractive to males only when these segments are protruded (calling), the duration of exposure varying from a few seconds to at least 90 minutes. Some females resume the calling position within seconds after retraction of the organs (81a).

Kellogg (199) reported in 1907 that the female silkworm moth (*Bombyx mori*) protrudes a paired scent organ from the hindmost abdominal segment. This gland is withdrawn into the body immediately after being touched by a male. The excised scent glands, but not the mutilated female, are highly attractive to the male. The structure of these glands has very recently been studied with the aid of the electron microscope by Steinbrecht and Schneider (325, 326) as well as Bounhiol (51b).

Nolte (249) could not find the sex attractant production glands of the female nun moth (*Porthetria monacha*) in the area of the ovipositor, although the excised abdomen lured males, whereas the wings and abdomen-free bodies were unattractive.

Amputation of the wings or antennae of a female gypsy moth (*Porthetria dispar*) does not affect her attractiveness to males, but males do not attempt to copulate with females freed of their entire abdomen or genital organs, and they are not successful in attempting to mate with those females deprived of abdominal scales and wings. The abdominal extremity of the female is therefore the attractive organ. Female abdomens excised at 9 p.m. and placed in a vessel containing three freshly-emerged males caused great agitation in these males by 10 p.m. (261).

Female webbing clothes moths (*Tineola biselliella*) could be observed in a "calling" pose, protruding and retracting their ovipositor and vibrating the tip of this organ. The excised female abdomen was attractive to males but the head and thorax was not (282).

Production of attractant by female *Diprion similis* appears to result from some as yet undefined site in the abdomen. A study of the gross external morphology failed to reveal specific gland openings that might be associated with production of the attractant (77).

The scent glands of male lepidopterous insects are present on the body or the wings (346). The simplest type is hairy, pierced by a single canal (as in *Eurytides protesilaus*), or numerous canals (as in *Argynnis*), or the surface is covered with openings as in a sieve. In Pierids and Lycaenids the secretory organs are located on the wings (167).

In 1902, Illig (174) published a masterly treatise describing his work on the anatomy and physiology of the odor glands of male butterflies; he also reviewed the subject. Beautiful colored plates illustrated his findings which are described in detail. The wings are the usual location for these organs in the male. However, in those butterflies that ordinarily fly by vigorous wing movements, such as the sphingids, the organs are situated in the abdomen, as shown in Table 3. In many cases the odor is the same as that of the flowers frequented by these insects, but there is no doubt that they are meant for use in sexual life. By vibrating the wings vigorously the male spreads the odor. Among those butterflies that fly during the day and mate in daylight, color may play a considerable part in sexual attraction, but among those flying at night and mating during darkness, odor is the prime attractant. Exotic butterflies, such as *Danaus* and *Euploea*, that fly during the day but have very highly developed odor organs on both wings and abdomen, probably must compete with the highly odorous flowers in their hot, tropical world.

Reichenau (269), investigating the scent of the male sphinx moth, *Sphinx ligustri*, supposed the scent material to be pressed by muscular action from the gland into the hairs or scales and

TABLE 3.   LOCATION OF THE ODOR ORGANS IN MALE
            BUTTERFLIES.

Location	Insects
Scattered on wings	*Pieris napi, Lycaena* spp.
Scales on wings	*Euploea, Terias hecabe fimbriata, Colias edusa*
Costal margins of wings	*Syrichtus malvae, Erynnis tages*
Wing folds	*Danaus plexippus, Panlymnas (Danaus) chrysippus*
Legs (tibia)	*Hepialus hectus*
Legs (tibia and femur)	*Pechipogon barbalis*
Base of abdomen	*Acherontia atropos, Sphinx ligustri*
Tips of abdomen	*Danaus plexippus, Euploea*

then from there diffused to the atmosphere through their apices. He also maintained that the scales were provided with capillary tubes in which the scent substance was held in the form of bubbles. These bubbles were doubtless the chitinous reticulum which is quite evident in the scales of *Ephestia cautella* and which probably holds the secretion within its meshes.

The anatomy and physiology of the scent gland of male *Hepialus hectus* was described in 1902 by Deegener (87). The pineapplelike scent of the secretion of these glands is an attractant for the female.

Males of *Achroea grisella* exude a strong aromatic odor that attracts and excites the female. The substance possessing this odor is formed mainly by the thorax and, to some extent, by the abdomen, but not by other parts of the body. Tufts of hair present on each side of the end abdominal segments serve to disperse the odor into the atmosphere (217).

Wing glands in males of *Aphomia gularis, Galleria mellonella, Plodia interpunctella,* and *Ephestia elutella* secrete odorous substances (27). Those substances produced by *Aphomia* and *Galleria* attract the female, and in the other species increase the female's excitement before copulation. These wing glands are absent in *Ephestia kühniella*. By vibrating the wings, the male disperses the odor.

Barth (29) compared the anatomy and the physiology of the male sex attractant organs in *Argynnis paphia, A. adippe,* and *A. aglaja.* These organs, situated on the wings, secrete an odorous chemical substance that excites the female in preparation for copulation.

The mandibular glands of virgin queen honey bees are suggested as a possible source of an odor attracting drones for mating (271), although extirpation of these glands does not necessarily render a virgin queen incapable of mating (242). Supplementary stimuli such as vision may be utilized by drones to locate virgin queens in flight.

Whereas 90% of normal female *Leucophaea* cockroaches accept a male within 26 days after emergence, only 30% of allatectomized females accept a male in this time (111). Mating in this insect apparently depends on the presence and activity of the corpora allata. This failure of allatectomized females to mate may depend on an alteration of their ability to perceive a chemical odor produced by the male which stimulates the female to feed on his tergal glands; unless the female responds in this way, mating does not occur. This chemical odor is perceived by the female with her antennae. Tergal feeding stimulates the male to copulate. Although allatectomized female *Diploptera* are courted and mate as readily as normal females, the females of this insect play a passive role during courtship (283).

Lhoste and Roche (224a) found that the two glands that probably produce the attractant in the male Mediterranean fruit fly are located in the last (seventh) abdominal segment. The attractive substance is diffused from these glands to the surface of an erectile anal ampoule formed by pulsating pressure from the posterior portion of the rectum.

Males of *Harpobittacus australis* and *H. nigriceps* (scorpion flies) attract the females by means of a scent produced in vesicles located between tergites 6–7 and 7–8 of the abdomen, which expand and contract rhythmically. These vesicles do not appear to have any associated scent reservoirs and seem to consist of a specialized intertergal membrane, the cells of which presumably discharge their secretion directly onto the membrane surface (51).

Gupta (151, 152) described the anatomy of the abdominal scent glands of Heteroptera and suggested that their function is primarily defensive in the nymph and both defensive and sexual in the adult.

CHAPTER SIX

THE MECHANISM
OF ATTRACTANT PERCEPTION

It has long been known that chemical insect attractants, especially the sex attractants, are detected by means of sense organs located mainly in the antennae (in the case of the Lepidoptera, the antennae are probably the sole organs of chemoreception). Hauser (161), in 1880, reviewed the subject of insect olfaction, beginning with the work of Lefebvre (221) in 1838. Hauser described in detail the anatomy of the antennae of species in the orders Orthoptera, Neuroptera, Hemiptera, Diptera, Lepidoptera, Coleoptera, and Hymenoptera; he also reported that males of *Saturnia pavonia* and *Porthetria dispar* deprived of their antennae never mated. In such species the male is often able to locate a female from a considerable distance, and his olfactory organs, situated on the plumelike antennae, are highly sensitive (184a, 331).

That the olfactory receptors are usually located on or in the antennae was substantiated by many investigators since Hauser's work was published. A few of their interesting reports will be described here.

In 1900, Mayer (232) reported that male promethea moths immediately flew from 100 feet away to a clear glass battery jar, covered with mosquito netting, containing five females. When the jar was inverted and sand was packed around its mouth to prevent the escape of air, males were no longer attracted. Males were also attracted to females wrapped loosely in cotton to make them invi-

59

sible; these males grasped the cotton with their abdominal claspers in typical copulatory attempts. Males were attracted by and mated with females whose wings had been replaced by those of males to deceive the latter. Mayer therefore concluded that sight was not involved in male attraction. He arranged a small wooden box containing females in such a way that air blown into the box emerged through a small chimney, and found that males were attracted to the top of the chimney, regardless of the presence of carbon disulfide and diethyl sulfide fumes in the immediate vicinity. Males released 5 feet from severed female abdomens flew directly to these abdomens, ignoring the remainder of the female body. Males deprived of their abdomen or whose spiracles were covered with glue were still attracted by females. However, males whose antennae were covered with shellac, glue, paraffin, Canada balsam, celloidin, or photographic paste did not seek a female and displayed no excitement even if held within one inch of a virgin female. Once the paste was washed away, the males once again responded to the female. Abbott (1) found that male promethea moths whose antennae had been coated with shellac flew irregularly and were unable to find a female in their immediate vicinity, even at a distance of only a few inches.

The great French naturalist, Fabre (115), in 1904, imprisoned a female emperor moth, still damp with the moisture of metamorphosis, under a gauze cover in his study. The same evening males "seemed to take possession of the house; about 40 male moths were flying round the gauze cover." This was repeated the following eight nights. The males appeared to fly with certainty to the house but, having arrived, were uncertain as to the precise location of the attractive object, and final discovery was left to a vague and hesitating search. The position of the cage could be changed and the female even imprisoned in a drawer, out of sight, without thwarting the males in their quest. Conditions were unfavorable for flight in that the weather was stormy and the dark house was surrounded by bushes and shrubs. Even if the female was surrounded by dishes of strong odorants such as napthalene and oils, she was still located by the males. Fabre also found that a spot on which a virgin female had recently rested, but from which she had been removed, was attractive to the males, particularly if the object on which she had rested was absorbant, such as cardboard, dust, or sand, and less so if it was hard and smooth like marble or metal. Excising the antennae rendered the males very much less skilled at finding the female.

Mayer and Soule (233) showed that male promethea and gypsy moths whose antennae were covered with flour paste would not mate with their respective females until the paste had been washed away with water. Normal males flew toward the females against the wind, frequently passing alongside and beyond the females. Under these conditions, the male would often remain poised on his wings, drifting back with the wind until he came to leeward of the female, when a few vigorous strokes would bring him toward her again.

Kellogg (199) reported in 1907 that male *Bombyx mori* with antennae intact but eyes blackened found females immediately, whereas those lacking antennae but able to see could not locate a female. Males possessing only a right antenna and exposed within 3 to 4 inches of a "calling" female circled repeatedly to the right until coming in contact with her; those lacking a right antenna circled to the left. This behavior was confirmed by Sengün (308) who also showed that, in the absence of air movement, normal males sometimes detected females from a distance of 5, but not 7, cm, whereas females could be located from a distance of 25–150 cm with moving air. Besides confirming the foregoing, Nakazema (247) reported that male *B. mori* with both antennae removed responded to females 76% less often than normal specimens. Coating the antennae with vaseline reduced the response somewhat. Minor olfactory regions were given as the basal portions of the wings and the labial palpi. Chemoreceptors of the male silkworm moth are evenly distributed throughout the antennae, as determined by removing different numbers of antennal joints (81). The perceptive distance decreases with the removal of increasing numbers of segments.

In describing the courtship of the polyphemus moth, Rau (267) reported that during sexual excitement the antennae of males are erect and alert, while on other occasions they are drooping and limp. Male cecropia moths with half of each antenna removed will mate, but mating does not occur with males completely lacking antennae (265).

According to Prüffer (261), male gypsy moths deprived of their wings, wing scales, abdominal scales, one antenna, or the tips of both antennae, or whose eyes are covered are able to find the females and mate, although those deprived of their wings have difficulty getting next to the female. Males deprived of both antennae show no interest in females.

Male pink bollworm moths with both antennae removed do

not respond to the female's attractive scent, but males with one antenna or with only part of the antenna clipped off respond readily (38).

Valentine (340) found that antennae-less male *Tenebrio molitor* never responded to a female and had to be placed directly on the female's back before copulatory reflexes asserted themselves. Application of paraffin oil to male antennae also prevented his response. A male with one antenna removed reacts by swerving off in an arc to the side bearing the remaining appendage, but he still responds to the female's odor; however, he is incapable of following the lure when it is set in motion. The same circus motion was elicited by coating one antenna with oil. Removal of the maxillary palpi had no effect on male response to the lure. Removal of various lengths of the antennae showed that the male organs operative in the discovery of the female are located chiefly in the terminal four segments of the antennae. Valentine concluded that it is reasonable to suppose that the peg organs found on these terminal segments are operative in the response of the male to the female odor. These results are in direct contradiction to the conclusions reached by McIndoo (234) in 1915. He reported that, beyond a doubt, none of the antennal organs of beetles serve as olfactory sites, and that the olfactory pores on the wings and legs are well adapted anatomically for receiving odor stimuli, since the peripheral ends of their sense fibers come into direct contact with the external air. However, McIndoo's tests were not conducted with females or their scent, the odorous substances used being peppermint, thyme, and wintergreen oils, pennyroyal and spearmint leaves and stems, and decayed matter from *Harpalus pennsylvanica* beetles.

Among the Lymexelonidae (beetles), the male has either an extraordinarily developed second joint to the maxillary palp or branched antennae. If the palpal joint is removed, he is no longer attracted by the female. Male *Hylecoetus dermestoides* having their feathery maxillary palpi coated with a film of gum mastic became inactive and would not mate with females in their vicinity. After the mastic was removed with alcohol they quickly became active and began to mate. The females, on the other hand, have a very simple type of maxillary palpi and antennae. Germer (136) concluded that the male detects the female with his maxillary palpi, which are well supplied with nerve stalks.

Male wasps (*Habrobracon juglandis*) whose abdomens had been removed or covered with lacquer could no longer locate the females

(246) and failed to show the premating excitement characteristic of normal males in the presence of females (148). Such abnormal males wandered aimlessly about and bumped against one another, although they were in the immediate vicinity of a female. When such a male accidentally came in contact with a female he would mount and copulate by reflex reaction, without exhibiting wing-flipping. No sexual excitement was shown by males whose antennae had been coated with celloidin, while males blinded by coating the eyes with asphaltum black behaved normally, showing excitement in the presence of females and mating successfully. Males whose abdomens had been removed responded normally to females and attempted to mount (149).

Abbott (2) attempted to determine if the antennae of male *Megarhyssa lunator* function in bringing the sexes together. Males whose antennae had been frozen by spraying with ethyl chloride were clipped on a wing to mark them, and released. Over a 2-week period, 11 of 16 released males returned to find the females, leading Abbott to conclude that the antennae are not used in bringing together the sexes. Males deprived of their antennae by excision also managed to locate the females (1).

Gara (133) showed that both male and female *Ips confusus* beetles freed of one antenna showed a 50% decrease in response to frass made attractive by male feeding, as compared with the response of intact beetles; removal of both antennae prevented the assembling response.

Drosophila victoria males produce an attractant (or aphrodisiac) for the females. Virgin females deprived of their antennae failed to accept males' overtures owing to their failure to receive olfactory stimuli; nevertheless, males attempted to copulate with antennae-less females despite the females' objections (319).

Although Riley (275), in 1894, conceded that the olfactory organs in lepidopterous insects are located in the antennae, he stated that there is good evidence (without citing such evidence) that in some hymenopterous insects the olfactory organ is localized in an ampulla at the base of the tongue.

Minnich (237) and Abbott (1) published reviews of the location and physiology of insect olfactory organs, reporting that the antennae are not the only sites of these organs, although others had not definitely been located. A thorough search of a number of detailed reviews of insect olfactory chemoreception prepared by Marshall (230), Dethier and Chadwick (93), Dethier (91, 92), Götz (145), Hecker (163), Chauvin (80), and Wright (365a) shows that, beyond a doubt, insects use their antennae in locating the opposite sex, although the maxillary and labial palpi, legs, and ovipositors may also be used.

The sites of insect olfactory reception in the antenna have been found to be various types of sensilla. Schneider (295), in his detailed review of insect antennae, defines a sensillum as "a specialized area of the integument, consisting of formative cells . . . , the sensory nerve cells and, in some cases, auxiliary cells." The very numerous sensilla may be classified into fifteen main groups, with sexual chemoreception, particularly in the lepidopterous insects, being assigned mainly to sensilla basiconica (sensory pegs or cones possessing one to several nerve fibers) and sensilla coeloconica (sensory pit-pegs or thin-walled cones situated on the floor of depressions in the antennal cuticle, and innervated by a bundle of nerve fibers) (290, 294a, 294b).

Schenk (288), in 1903, described the anatomy and histology of sexual differences in the antennae of four Lepidoptera and ten Hymenoptera. The nervous system of the antennae in male and female *Saturnia pyri* was studied by Prüffer (262). The principle of the nervous system is the same in both, but the female antenna is characterized by a smaller number of nerve cells as seen by a reduction of the antennal length.

In 1937, Barth (28) reported on a study of the anatomy of the antennae in *Plodia interpunctella* and *Aphomia gularis*. The antennae of both male and female *Plodia* consist of forty-eight segments plus a ring and a shaft segment, each of which is provided with sensilla coeloconica and sensilla styloconica. Excision of the palpi in *Plodia* and *Aphomia* does not prevent sexual excitement in the male. Removal of the entire right and half of the left antenna still permits the male to respond, since it leaves him with 81 coeloconica and 9 styloconica sensilla, but removal of the entire right and three-fourths of the left antenna prevents reception (35 coeloconica and 2 styloconica). Removing three-fourths of each antenna prevents reception (68 coeloconica and 4 styloconica), but a response is still elicited after one-half of each antenna is removed (leaving 162 coeloconica and 18 styloconica). Barth found that the typical male sexual dance is elicited within 1 to 2 seconds in a container that had previously held a female; apparently the sensilla styloconica come into play at first followed by the sensilla coeloconica. Male *Plodia* antennae possess 320 sensilla coeloconica, whereas female antennae possess 274.

Vogel (342) reported that the male honeybee antenna contains many more sensilla than that of the female or worker.

According to Ford (128), the attractants of both male and female moths are perceived by the antennae, which contain great numbers of "end organs" capable of being stimulated by volatile substances (scents) carried in the air. Several types of these structures exist, but in general they are minute cups of the chitinous surface in the center of which is a projection connected to a nerve cell. Antennae of female moths are relatively simple, chiefly engaged in registering the aphrodisiac scent of the male produced when he is close at hand; they consist of jointed rods only occasionally provided with short side branches. Antennae of the males of some species are much more elaborate, with brushlike extensions along both sides so that their surface is greatly increased. On the other hand, the antennae of butterflies are never "feathered" or pectinated; they always end in a knob while those of moths rarely do so and never in forms without the frenulum.

In four reports published between 1956 and 1959, Schneider, et al. (290, 297, 298, 299) described in great detail the morphology of *Bombyx mori* antennae and their function in chemoreception. Using electrophysiological methods, wherein tiny silver chloride-coated electrodes (56) were inserted into the freshly excised male antenna which was further connected through an amplifier to an oscilloscope, Schneider (290, 296) succeeded in recording action potentials from the antennae. On stimulation with natural *Bombyx* sex attractant, a characteristic response (EAG or electroantenogram) appeared, whereas other olfactory stimuli or drugs resulted in different forms of electroantenograms; the amplitude of the EAG is directly related to the concentration of the attractant tested. When the olfactory stimulus is extract of female *Bombyx* sex attractant, electrical activity increases in the male antenna but not in that of the female, whereas activity increases in both sexes when the stimuli are cyclohexanone or sorbyl alcohol. Many compounds in high concentration elicit an EAG (ether, ethanol, propanol, butanol, or xylene), but only the sex attractant elicits an EAG at extreme dilution. Electrophysiological measurement of attractants was reviewed by Schneider (292) in 1961 in a trade journal of very limited circulation, and the technique was utilized by Morita and Yamashita (240) in 1961 to record receptor potentials from sensilla basiconica in the antennae of *Bombyx mori* larvae.

Schneider's assumption that the EAG is essentially the sum of many olfactory receptor potentials recorded more or less simultaneously by an electrode located in the sensory epithelium has received experimental support, since it is now known (293) that the single unit receptor potential appears to be identical. The electrophysiological procedure has been extended to a number of Lepidoptera (*Callosamia promethea, Hyalophora colleta, H. euryalus, Antheraea pernyi, Rothschildia orizaba, Samia cynthia, Porthetria dispar*) (291, 293, 294, 299a), the carrion beetle (*Necrophorus humator*) (49), and the American cockroach (*Periplaneta americana*) (50). The species specificity of the sexual attracting substances of seven saturniids was checked by the EAG method (293). There were no significant differences in the EAG's of a male antenna using the female attractant-producing glands of different species as stimuli, but the effect of the related saturniids on the male *Bombyx* antenna was much smaller than that of the female *Bombyx* gland; neither the female *Bombyx* gland nor the synthetic *Bombyx* sex attractant (bombykol) elicited a response in the antenna of any of the saturniid males checked. Although the antennae of males and females responded to concentrated essential oils (wintergreen, clove) with an EAG, no antenna of any of the female saturniids or *Bombyx* responded to any of the glands. Bombykol showed an electrical response threshold between 10^8 and 10^{14} times lower than those of the other three *cis-trans* isomers of this structure. Contrary to earlier work with concentrated lures (290), the EAG threshold has been shown to be much higher than the behavior threshold using the pure substance.

Schneider (294) found that the exposure of excised male antennae to a sex attractant held on the tip of a glass rod could be greatly refined by the use of a living mounted male exposed to the test substance impregnated on a fluted filter paper in a short glass tube. Under these circumstances it was possible to record EAG's for many hours or days, instead of only 1 to 2 hours, and the cartridges were easily exchanged during the course of an experiment. The reaction of a male *Bombyx* to bombykol was practically constant from a threshold below 10^{-10} μg to about 10^{-4} μg; with higher concentrations the reaction intensity first rose slowly and then very rapidly. From this response, Schneider deduced that the insect could not distinguish between different molecular densities with great sensitivity in the lower concentration range, but the sensitivity is much greater in the higher range. In support of this hypothesis was his finding that dissected glands of female *Bombyx* were electrophysiologically as effective as filter paper containing 10^{-2} to 10 μg bombykol; this concentration range was exactly where the gradient of the curve was steepest and where odor intensity discrimination was expected to be optimal. The gypsy moth male antenna showed the expected EAG stimulus-response curve when exposed to the pure *Porthetria dispar* sex attractant, rising slowly and then more sharply with ascending concentrations; a saturation effect could not be observed, even with the pure attractant in the highest concentration tested. Both the dextrorotatory and levorotatory forms of this attractant showed the same threshold (10^{-2} μg). The male *Bombyx* antenna gave no EAG response above the control when exposed to the *Porthetria* attractant. The female *Bombyx* antenna showed no EAG response to the gland or to synthetic bombykol, indicating that the female moth does not possess the specific receptor type for detecting its own attractant. However, the antenna of female *Periplaneta americana* gave an EAG response to its own sex attractant which was approximately 50% as large as that given by the male antenna (50). The threshold concentration to the male roach antenna was approximately 0.1 μg of pure attractant.

According to Kettlewell (202) male moths assemble or fly to females only upwind, gauging the direction by contrasting the number of molecules striking each antenna per unit of time. The volatility is greater at higher temperatures, with considerable loss of scent occurring in hot sunlight by convection currents. Immediately to the windward side of the male is a "negative zone," males flying directly into this zone showing behavior varying with the species. In *Endromis versicolora*, a male striking this zone wheels around and returns several times close to the ground; in *Parasemia plantaginis*, the males alight on the ground and proceed for the rest of the journey on foot or by fluttering through the undergrowth.

Laboratory and field tests conducted by Schwinck (301, 303, 304) and reported in 1954, 1955, and 1958 showed that a pure odor attraction of male *Bombyx mori* by the female could only be demonstrated for close orientation, resulting from trial and error as successive differential perceptions. At a greater distance the attractant has only an excitatory effect, unorientated distant searching being initiated by the odor stimulus. Estimation of the concentration gradients for open room diffusion, supporting the test results, showed this gradient not to be the orientating factor for distance attraction. Air streams containing the attractant showed a much greater orientation for males than did the attractant in the absence of air streams; the males move in proportional linear orbits against the wind. The odor stimulus is only the cause of the streaming orientation, and the directional factor is merely the air stream and not a concentration gradient. Odor stimulation acts as a constant stimulator of streaming orientation; a strong diminution of attractant concentration leads to elimination of stream orientation. It was concluded that the sequence is (1) random searching flight by the male, (2) orientation against the wind when the female odor is detected, and (3) upwind flight; if the male strays from the wind stream, he resumes random searching flight until the odor is again detected. The female sexual odor is thus not an attractant for distance orientation, but only an excitant to release another orientation mechanism; it becomes a true attractant only over a short distance from the male. Laboratory tests with *B. mori, Porthetria dispar, P. monacha, Orgyia antiqua,* and *Lasiocampa quercus* males with partial antennal amputation showed that the sensilla styloconica played no part in male orientation to the female odor.

Schwinck's theory of a guidance mechanism directing the course of the male toward a receptive female is supported by laboratory observations with *Trichoplusia ni* (312). Males remain in the typical resting position until they are exposed to air carrying the sex pheromone—when the antennae are "raised and brought slightly forward of a plane perpendicular to the body axis." The wings are then extended and vibrated and the male flies toward the source of the odorous air stream. The positive orientation of the male to the air current may be facilitated at close range by air movement from a receptive female's vibrating wings.

Wilson (51a, 354, 354a) and his associates deduced the shape and size of the ellipsoidal space within which male moths can be attracted under natural conditions. With a moderate wind blowing, "the active space has a long axis of thousands of meters and a transverse axis parallel to the ground of more than 200 meters at the widest point" (354). The dimensions of active space of gyplure for male gypsy moths with winds of various velocities were deduced from linear measurements and general gas-diffusion models.

Casida, et al. (77) reported that the approach of the male introduced pine sawfly (*Diprion similis*) to the attractive female is characterized by a zig-zag pattern decreasing in amplitude as the "point" source is approached. Within several feet of the attractant source, the males usually proceed slowly in locating the attractant or occasionally go directly to the active material.

The manner in which a moth finds a mate has inspired biologists and biochemists to propound a number of theories about the mechanism of olfaction in both moths and man. In 1894, Riley (276) reported experiments in which he liberated a male cynthia moth in the park a mile and a half away from a female moth in his window; the following morning the two were together. He tried to account for the attraction of insects for one another from a distance by a sort of telepathy; he stated, "this power would depend neither upon scent nor upon hearing in the ordinary understanding of these senses, but rather on certain subtle vibrations as difficult for us to apprehend as is the exact nature of electricity." Although Fabre's experiments (115, 116, 117) certainly indicated strongly that female moths attract the males by odor, he could not bring himself to believe that odor could draw moths from hundreds of yards or even miles away. He therefore postulated the existence of another sense, unknown to us, which by a vibrational stimulus warned the males from afar. He felt that something about the moth vibrates, causing waves capable of propagation to distances incompatible with an actual diffusion of matter.

In 1913, Teudt (329) presented a summary of several theories of olfaction, comprising (1) odor particles dissolved by the mucus, (2) intramolecular vibration of odorous substances when the molecules come in contact with the nerves, and (3) rhythmic axial revolution of the molecule, dependent on the number, position, and quality of the combined atoms in the molecule. As a result of his own observations, Teudt explained the attraction of female moths to males in the presence of very odorous materials, such as naphthalene, by saying that the vibrations in the male's odor receptor organs do not react to the vibrations of the naphthalene odor; he concluded that odor detection takes place by electron vibrations.

Observations over more than ten years led Dyson (100, 101, 102) to conclude that odor must be related to a characteristic molecular vibration pattern, and he assigned certain odors to certain Raman frequencies ("osmic" frequencies) in the general range of 1500–3000 cm^{-1}. This was followed in 1950 with a hypothesis by Duane and Tyler (96) in which the attractant in the female moth emits infrared radiations picked up by sensitive receivers located in the male's antennae. These investigators measured the radiation from female polyphemus and cecropia moths using a recording infrared spectrophotometer and found a definite pattern in the region from 3–11 μ. By means of a small thermocouple buried in the fine fur of the female's thorax, it was determined that an active female raised her temperature as much as 11° above that of the room by vibrating her wings or moving her legs; thus, she radiated energy at a greater rate than her surroundings. Duane and Tyler also measured the lengths of antennal hairs of male cecropia moths and determined them to be between 40–80 μ; all variations in the length of the hairs appeared to be close to 4 μ or multiples thereof. This led the investigators to speculate in the following way: "It is noteworthy that four microns is one-half the wave length of eight microns which is well within the emission band of the female. Does this mean that the male Cecropia moth has a tuned antenna array which is his receptor for locating the female?"

Callahan (74) supports an electromagnetic radiation force of attraction between the sexes, based on flight behavior and configuration of the antennae in flight, as measured in the infrared region.

Nolte (249), in 1940, had attempted to discount a radiation theory of insect olfaction by citing Prüffer's tests in which live female gypsy moths placed in a lead cylinder impervious to radioactive rays still lured males, whereas females kept under a glass did not.

By means of a panel of observers used to select by smell sixteen compounds with an odor resembling that of nitrobenzene, Wright (358, 363) set up a theory of odor based on its correlation with a pattern of molecular vibrations below 1000 cm^{-1} wave number as studied by means of Raman frequencies. He claimed that this refuted Dyson's theory of molecular vibration by osmic frequencies in the range 1500–3000 cm^{-1}. In a reply, Dyson (103) admitted an error in assuming the frequencies concerned to be those in the higher Raman ranges, but claimed that Wright's results proved that his (Dyson's) original hypothesis correlating odor specificity with molecular vibration was sound in principle. In 1957, Wright (359) extended his theory of low-frequency molecular vibration to insect olfaction, claiming that the nerve cells of the male's olfactory end organ contain a pigment of unknown constitution. "When an odorous molecule whose vibrational frequency matches that of the pigment molecule becomes linked to it by forces of adsorption, or something of the sort, the frequency of vibration of the combined system pigment-plus-odorous molecule is not the same as the frequency of the pigment alone, even though these two frequencies are identical when they are not linked to each other" (359). The theory presupposes some kind of direct interaction between the vibration of the odorous molecules and the male's receptor organs. It predicts that in a group of dissimilar chemicals that can act as sex attractants for the males of a certain insect, there will be present certain frequencies that will be absent in biologically inactive substances, other things being equal (360, 364). Attempting to explain how the male insect follows a scent, Wright claimed that an insect in free flight and before it enters an odor cloud probably searches by flying a series of rather long, zig-zag paths. When it enters the cloud, its tendency to turn is inhibited as long as the interval between pulses tends to decrease. If it starts to move out of the cloud or away from the source, the interval between pulses will increase, releasing the inhibition on the tendency to turn. This would cause abandonment of a fixed flight path to make a series of short, violent zig-zags until it once more locates a path in which the pulse interval tends to decrease. "Where sex attractants are involved, and these are the scents which operate over great distances, the emitting insect, usually the female, could actively assist the guiding process by emitting the scent in a series of short puffs" (361). Wright (362) completed a discussion of the theory, as it might apply to a number of insect attractants, with this statement: "The vibrational theory of odour is consistent with what is known of the substances which are demonstrably perceptible to various insect species by what appears to be an olfactory process. As it stands, the evidence does not confirm the theory, but the fact that the theory enables certain rather specific predictions to be made opens the way to an experimental test."

In 1964, Wright (365b) speculated that insects probably need a *combination* of primary odors to evoke a response, rather than a *single* odor. He theorized that the sex attractant scents, in most cases, are probably due to a mixture of substances which must all be present to compete with indifferent molecules on the sensory surface of the insect's receptors. Although Wright cites a few examples of insect sex attractants in which this might possibly be correct, most of the evidence thus far collected makes it almost certain that naturally occurring sex attractants in most species of insects are single highly specific compounds.

Independently of Wright, Laithwaite (218) in 1960 proposed a radiation theory of moth assembling. Pointing out that air turbulence is practically continuous, he claimed that it is difficult for the followers of an olfactory theory of assembling to explain that "males will assemble to a virgin female both up and down wind," flying in a direct line. Laithwaite claimed to have substantiated this by experimental observation with released males of the common vapourer moth (*Orgyia antiqua*) and to have found that males released from a distance of 10 feet immediately converged on an empty box, a fertilized female, a dead female, eggs, and an empty female pupal case, whereas those released 100 yards away were not attracted by any of these objects despite the fact that a virgin female will attract males from this distance. The male's antenna was compared to an electromagnetic aerial, with the spacing (0.2–0.02 mm) of the pectinations indicating an operating wavelength in the far infrared band. Females placed in an extremely fine-mesh wire gauze box, which allowed scent particles to pass through but would effectively screen electromagnetic waves, attracted males from a short distance only. In a detailed reply, Kettlewell (203) pointed out that Laithwaite had cited no positive evidence to support his radiation theory and had been misled, by low wind velocities and countereddies, into believing that males are capable of downwind assembling to a female. The total substance of Laithwaite's evidence, according to Kettlewell, was his observation of the similarity between radar antennae and assembling male moth antennae.

A stereochemical theory of olfaction proposed recently by Amoore (15, 16, 17) may be of considerable assistance in the future determination of the olfactory mechanism in insects (170). The following are put forth as primary odors: camphoraceous, pungent, ethereal, floral, pepperminty, musky, putrid. Certain definite molecular properties characterize all compounds with the same primary odor and distinguish them from all compounds with different primary odors. Thus, the camphoraceous odor is exhibited by spherical molecules about 7 Å in diameter, the musky odor by disk-shaped molecules about 10 Å in diameter, the floral odor by kite-shaped molecules, pepperminty odors by wedge-shaped molecules with a polar group near the point of the wedge, ethereal odors by very small or thin molecules, pungent odors by electrophilic molecules, and putrid odors by nucleophilic molecules. Other characteristic odors are considered to be complex odors due to the molecules fitting two or more different primary odor receptor sites. If a chemical is volatile and its molecules have the appropriate configuration to fit closely into the receptor site, then a nervous impulse is initiated, possibly through a mechanism involving disorientation and depolarization of the receptor cell membrane. The theory, which shows good agreement with actual experience (286), is discussed in detail by Amoore et al. (18, 19).

CHAPTER SEVEN

INFLUENCE OF AGE OF THE INSECT ON PRODUCTION OF AND RESPONSE TO SEX ATTRACTANTS

Although many species of insects may produce and emit sex attractants for their entire life span, beginning at the time of emergence, many others do not attain sexual maturity until they reach a certain age and the attractant production may cease some time before natural death of the insect. Similarly, the attracted sex may or may not be sexually mature at emergence. It is therefore necessary that such factors be taken into account in attempting to demonstrate the presence of chemical sex attraction in any insect, as the following survey clearly shows.

LEPIDOPTERA

One-day-old females of *Lobesia* (*Polychrosis*) *botrana* and *Clysia ambiguella* are more attractive to males than are 2-day-old females, although virgin females remain attractive for their normal life span (9–13 days) (139). Laboratory experiments showed that a 2-day-old female *C. ambiguella* immediately excited a male brought to her vicinity (138).

Although Fabre (115) reported many years earlier that female *Lasiocampa quercus* must be 2 or 3 days of age before they can attract males, Dufay (97) demonstrated that newly emerged females are quite attractive to males.

Newly emerged lesser peach tree borer moths can become attractive to males as soon as they are ready for flight, usually 25–35 minutes after emergence, but only about 59% of all females tested prove to be attractive (81a). They remain attractive up to 5 days.

Female sugar cane borer moths begin to emit their attractant soon after emergence and are most attractive during the first 3 days of life, after which attractiveness decreases with age (257a).

Female *Prodenia litura* and *Agrotis ypsilon* do not release their sex attractants until they are at least 1 hour old (123). The cells of the secretory abdominal glands producing the scent are larger in 1- and 2-day-old females than in those 3–5 days old; indeed, these cells begin to shrink and decrease in size after the second day (156).

Male *Plodia interpunctella*, 1 day old, placed in a dish in which a 1-day-old virgin female had rested, immediately began a courtship dance and attempted to copulate. Females are not attractive until they are at least 3 hours old, and males do not respond until they are at least 50 minutes old. Although females 5 days old were not attractive, a weak male response was evoked by 15-day-old females (223). Chemical fractions obtained from the crude extract of female abdominal glands were tested for activity on males 40–50 hours old (367). Richards and Thomson (273) reported that adults of *Ephestia* and *Plodia* are ready for mating a very short time after emergence, almost as soon as the wings are dry.

Female *Cacoecia murinana* moths placed in small cages in the field were attractive from the day of emergence to a maximum age of 11 days, luring large numbers of males but no females (130).

According to Ouye and Butt (251), female pink bollworm moths 1–6 days old were attractive to males, but low catches of 1–3-day-old males were obtained. Berger et al. (38) found that females yielded active extracts regardless of age.

Virgin female Nantucket pine tip moths (*Rhyacionia frustrana*) are most attractive early in their life span, becoming unattractive as they age. The maximum age for an attractive female is 9 days (357).

Virgin males 4 days old were used by Ignoffo et al. (173) to test the response evoked by an extract of the abdominal tips of female cabbage looper moths (*Trichoplusia ni*). Although a small proportion of females was capable of mating on the night following emergence, most females mated for the first time on the second or third nights (314).

The majority of virgin female tobacco hornworm moths do not become attractive to males until the second night following emergence, and even then some individuals are not attractive. Vigor and vitality of the females are important factors in the production of attractant as well as responsiveness of the males. Individual testing appears to be the only sure way of ascertaining attractiveness (9). Female tobacco budworm moths must be at least 4 days old before they can attract males (135b).

Male and female *Bombyx mori* do not fly and are eager to mate immediately following emergence (199, 227). Steinbrecht (325a) has recently shown that the female *B. mori* is already attractive in the last days of its pupal stage. On the other hand, males and females of the related gypsy moth (*Porthetria dispar*) become sexually mature 2–3 days after emergence; males emerge several days before the females (261). Although newly emerged females are very weakly attractive, the amount of attractant emitted rapidly increases during the first day after emergence and remains constant until death (287). Tests conducted in a garden showed that, of 300 male gypsy moths released, 156 were attracted to a newly emerged virgin female, 6 were attracted to a 7-day-old virgin female who had already oviposited, 2 were attracted to a mated female who had oviposited, and 52 were attracted to a female who had mated immediately before but had not yet oviposited (263). Virgin females bioassayed in the laboratory were maximally attractive at the end of the first hours of adulthood (45). Female nun moths (*Porthetria monacha*) were most attractive to males when 1–2 days old (177). Newly emerged females are very weakly attractive, the attraction becoming stronger in females 1–2 days of age; attraction almost disappears after mating and is completely gone by oviposition (13, 157). The female continues to attract for about 12 days, according to Hanno (157), with average maximum potency lasting for 8 days (119). Eidmann (107) claims that *P. monacha* females, as well as those of most of the spinners (including *Dasychira pudibunda* and *Dendrolimus pini*), in which the female possesses ripe eggs at emergence and which do not feed after emergence, are capable of mating immediately upon emergence.

Although Vöhringer (344) reported that the male wax moth (*Galleria mellonella*) begins to release an attractant for the female from his wing glands 12 hours following emergence, copulation was observed between males $1\frac{1}{2}$–2 hours old and females about 12 hours. Röller et al. (279) subsequently showed that the males develop a characteristic odor when they are 2–24 hours old; this odor reaches maximum strength during the evening hours.

COLEOPTERA

The scent attractive to both males and females is released only after emerging male *Ips confusus* have fed for several hours on new host material (ponderosa pine) and the gut has been filled (341).

Adult *Tenebrio molitor* are at least 10–12 days old before mating occurs (340).

HYMENOPTERA

Female introduced pine sawflies (*Diprion similis*) emerging from ground-level cocoons are usually mated by the time they have crawled part way up the stems of grasses; once mated, they no longer elicit a response from the males (83).

Male *Bracon hebetor* 24 hours old show a typical sexual response upon exposure to live or crushed females (149).

Adult *Macrocentrus ancylivora* usually copulate almost as soon as they emerge, although there are exceptions in which copulation does not occur until several hours afterward (122).

NEUROPTERA

Male *Osmylus chrysops* begin calling females 2 days after emergence (355).

CHAPTER EIGHT

INFLUENCE OF TIME OF DAY
ON SEX ATTRACTANT PRODUCTION
AND MATING

Since it is safe to assume that sex attractants and excitants in insects are produced only immediately before or during the period of the day in which mating normally occurs, it is extremely important that the effect of time of day on sex production be considered in investigations designed to demonstrate the existence or collection of these attractive substances.

LEPIDOPTERA

This order comprises many species (mainly moths) normally mating during the hours of darkness and many others (mainly butterflies) in which assembling and mating occur during daylight hours. Attempting to learn as much as possible about the mating habits of these insects, Götz (142) in 1941 devised the simple yet ingenious device shown in Figures 4a and 4b. This clock-operated turntable consisted of an iron tripod holding a clock mechanism whose hour axis moved a glue-covered aluminum dial of 32-cm diameter. Divided into 12 segments, the dial made a complete circle in 12 hours. The entire clock mechanism was closed at the top with a lead disc containing a covered opening to allow entrance of the male. To the underside of the tripod rim was fastened a number of metal containers in each of which was placed a virgin

(a)

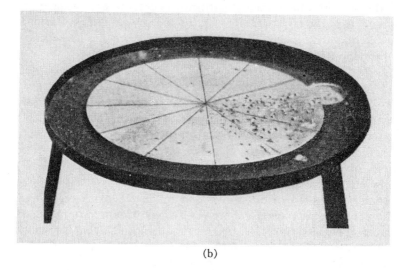

(b)

Figure 4. Clock-operated turntable. (a) side view, (b) top view. [From
B. Götz, *Umschau*, **45**, 779 (1941), Umschau Verlag, Frankfurt a. M.]

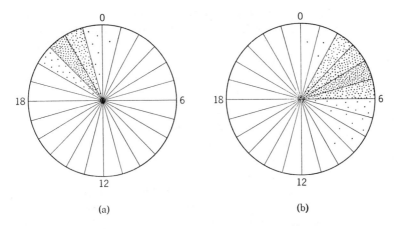

0   0

18   6   18   6

12   12

(a)   (b)

Figure 5. Time of day for mating of grape insects, as determined with the turntable. (a) for *Lobesia botrana* (b) for *Clysia ambiguella*. [From B. Götz, Umschau, **45**, 779 (1941), Umschau Verlag, Frankfurt a. M.]

female, whose odor could penetrate through a gauze covering over the opening. Males attracted to the females of their species remained fastened to that part of the turntable holding the female. Through the use of this apparatus, Götz found that this attraction occurs during evening hours (9 P.M. to midnight) (Figure 5a) with *Lobesia* (*Polychrosis*) *botrana* and in the early morning hours (2 to 6 A.M.) (Figure 5b) in the case of *Clysia ambiguella* (142, 143, 144, 145).

Fabre (117) found that hordes of males visited a captive female peacock moth (*Saturnia pavonia*) each evening between 8 and 10 o'clock, while a captive female lesser peacock moth (*S. pavonia minor*) was visited by a number of males between noon and 2 P.M. A female oak eggar moth (*Lasiocampa quercus*) attracted males at about 3 P.M.

Female *Parasemia plantaginis* attract their males during the day and assemble at dusk. The normal calling time of *Callimorpha dominula* is from midnight to 5 or 6 P.M., but a male was caught by a caged female at 11:15 P.M. The normal mating time of insects is greatly prolonged in the case of caged females (202).

Rau and Rau (268) determined the following assembling periods: 3:30–6:00 P.M. (mainly 4:00–4:30 P.M.) for *Callosamia promethea*, dawn for *Hyalophora* (*Samia*) *cecropia*, 9–12 P.M. and again from 3 A.M. to dawn for *Samia* (*Platysamia*) *cynthia*. Assembling of *Antheraea* (*Telea*) *polyphemus* is apparently not confined to one brief period of the night. Moonlight influences the period of flight in some species. Mayer (232) reported that the male promethea moth is attracted to the female between the hours of 2 P.M. and sunset. Soule (317) reported 4:00–4:30 A.M. as the hour of mating for the cecropia moth, and Rau (266) stated that "mating in this insect starts between midnight and morning and ends at those hours on the following day."

The female *Porthesia similis* is ready for mating about 1½ hours following emergence, which usually occurs at 7 A.M. (339). If unfertilized, she may continue protruding and retracting the ovipositor for days at the same rate until mating occurs.

The time of maximum natural attraction in lesser peach tree borer moths (*Synanthedon pictipes*) is from 9 to 11 A.M. (81a).

Male tobacco budworm moths (*Heliothis virescens*) are attracted to the females only in the early morning hours, between 4 A.M. and daylight (135b).

Standfuss (320) reported that a newly emerged female *Saturnia pavonia* moth attracted 127 males from a distance between 10:30 A.M. and 5:00 P.M. A new female does not usually protrude her ovipositor until the following day in order to increase her drawing power, although attraction and mating may occur without "calling." If unmated, she remains inactive all night until forenoon, then begins calling until evening (339).

The period of highest attractiveness for *Prodenia litura* is during the first 2 or 3 hours after darkness (353), and from dusk to midnight (or 6 P.M. to 2 A.M.) for *Cacoecia murinana* (130). Maximum mating activity occurs between 5 and 7 A.M. in *Solenobia triquetrella* (306), 10:30 P.M. to 3 A.M. in *Protoparce sexta* (9), and midnight to 4 A.M. or dawn in caged *Trichoplusia ni* (173, 313a). Sexual activity in the sugar cane borer moth (*Diatraea saccharalis*) is mostly confined to the hours between 1 and 4 A.M. (257a).

Although the male gypsy moth (*Porthetria dispar*) flies during the day, mating usually occurs during the evening and night hours (137, 261). Female abdomens excised at 9:00 P.M. and placed in a cage containing three newly emerged males caused great agitation among the males within one hour (261). Varying reports of peak male nun moth (*Porthetria monacha*) activity are 6:00 P.M. to 1:00 A.M., beginning at dusk (11, 13), 7 to 9 P.M. (249), and late afternoon and evening (137).

Males are attracted to female webbing clothes moths (*Tineola biselliella*) in the morning or evening (332) and to female Nantucket pine tip moths (*Rhyacionia frustrana*) in the evening (357).

Although male pink bollworm moths (*Pectinophora gossypiella*) are attracted to females in the field during darkness, those males reared in the laboratory under continuous illumination will respond readily at any time to an extract of the female abdomens (251).

The production of sex attractant by females of *Plodia interpunctella*, *Ephestia kühniella*, *Achroea grisella*, and *Galleria mellonella* does not appear to be restricted to specific hours (28).

It is obvious from the foregoing that lepidopterous insects exhibit specific but extremely varied times of courtship and mating.

COLEOPTERA

Numerous male June beetles (*Phyllophaga lanceolata*) fly from various directions during the hours of 6:30 and 11:30 A.M. and alight on the ground near a female (333).

The volatile substance responsible for mass attraction of both sexes to male *Ips confusus* is produced only during the initial period of attack on ponderosa pine logs, but the attraction shows a definite diurnal pattern at 8–10 A.M. and 2–6 P.M. (133, 341). Similarly, the response flight of both sexes of *Dendroctonus pseudotsuga* to the volatile substance produced by sexually mature, unmated females feeding on Douglas-fir phloem exhibits a distinct diurnal and seasonal pattern (284). Flight begins in the morning as soon as a threshold temperature of 68°F has been reached, attaining its peak around noon. Later in the season, high temperatures during midday always result in marked depression of flight. Concentrated flight ceases at sunset, even though the temperature may remain optimal for flight.

HYMENOPTERA

Attraction of male *Bracon hebetor* by females occurs during daylight (morning) hours (149).

A virgin female introduced pine sawfly (*Diprion similis*) set in the field at 11 A.M. attracted its first males within 30 seconds. Activity continued until 4 P.M., when a total of over 7000 males had been attracted. The greatest activity occurred between midnight and midafternoon (83).

DIPTERA

Greatest activity of female hessian flies (*Phytophaga destructor*) to attract males occurs in the early morning (76).

CHAPTER NINE

COLLECTION, ISOLATION, AND IDENTIFICATION OF THE SEX ATTRACTANTS

ORTHOPTERA

Periplaneta americana, American cockroach

Solutions of the attractant can be obtained by extracting with petroleum ether at room temperature papers on which virgin females have been kept. These extracts concentrated by vacuum distillation at 22°C (distillates collected in a freezing bath were not attractive to males) (349) were stable under refrigeration for several months (350). In order to obtain larger amounts of attractant, Wharton et al. (348) exposed many papers to virgin females which were then extracted with water. The extract was made alkaline and then acidified to pH 5.0–5.5, and heated until 60% had been distilled. The distillate was freed of fatty acids and repeatedly redistilled until the volume of the final distillate was convenient for complete extraction with isopentane. Purification and isolation of 28 μg of a pure attractant were accomplished by a combination of column and gas chromatography. The attractant was reported to be aliphatic and to contain ester carbonyl (348).

An improved method for collecting much larger quantities of the attractant was reported by Yamamoto (366). Virgin females (1000) were confined in a 10-gallon capacity milk can, and a stream of air (2 ft⁴/sec) was passed through the container and

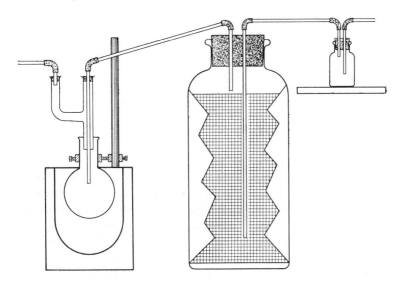

Figure 6. Apparatus for collection of sex attractant from cockroaches. [Redrawn and modified from R. Yamamoto, *J. Econ. Entomol.*, **56**, 119 (1963), Entomological Society of America, College Park, Md.]

into a receiver immersed in an alcohol-dry ice bath, as shown in Figure 6. The cellulose powder column absorbed uncondensed attractant which could be washed with organic solvent for recovery. A number of cans could be connected in series through a common air inlet.

The condensate obtained from approximately 10,000 females over a 9-month period, collected by Yamamoto's method, was chromatographed on silicic acid; elution with 10% ether in hexane, following successive elution with hexane and 3% ether in hexane, removed the attractant from the column completely. The pure attractant was obtained by steam distillation as 12.2 mg of a pale yellow liquid with a characteristic sweet odor; it elicited a response from males at levels below 10^{-14} μg (190). Gas chromatography of the attractant showed that it was pure and that it was obviously different from the substance with which Wharton's group (348) had been working. On the basis of physical and chemical data, the attractant was identified by Jacobson et al. (190) as 2,2-dimethyl-3-isopropylidenecyclopropyl propionate (I), but this structure has very recently been found to be incorrect by synthesis of an inactive compound having structure I (86a, 187a, 345a).

$$\begin{array}{ccc}
H_3C & & CH_3 \\
\diagdown & & \diagup \\
& C=C\!-\!-\!C & \\
\diagup & \diagdown\!\diagup & \diagdown \\
H_3C & C & CH_3 \\
& \diagup\diagdown & \\
H & OCCH_2CH_3 & \\
& \| & \\
& O &
\end{array}$$

(I)

Wharton et al. (347), in a critique of the work by Jacobson and co-workers (190), stated that collection of the attractant by extraction of filter papers gave three to five times more attractant per roach per day than did the air-collection method. They also stated that Jacobson's attractive material could not have been pure. However, Jacobson and Beroza (186), in a reply to this critique, put forth additional evidence to refute Wharton's claims.

The true structure of the sex attractant remains open.

HEMIPTERA

Lethocerus indicus, giant water bug

The clear liquid with a cinnamon odor produced by the adult male and which probably acts as an aphrodisiac for the female is obtained by opening the abdomen dorsally, removing the white tubules, pressing them in a glass, and filtering the press liquid (69). The clear, water-white liquid boils at 168–170° and possesses refractive index (n_D^{25}) 1.4160, unchanged after distillation. The infrared spectrum showed carbonyl absorption at 5.80μ and gave a positive hydroxamate test for an ester grouping. Saponification of the liquid with ethylmagnesium bromide gave acetic acid and an alcohol which was esterified with 4'-nitroazo-benzenecarboxylic acid chloride; the ester formed showed m.p. 128–129°. Oxidation of the double bond of the natural attractant, together with the foregoing data, identified the liquid attractant as *trans*-2-hexen-1-yl acetate (II). A synthetic sample of this material showed b.p. 165–166° and n_D^{25} 1.4173; its infrared spectrum lacked two small bands

$$CH_3(CH_2)_2CH=CHCH_2OCOCH_3$$

(II)

(8.50 and 9.25μ) present in the spectrum of the natural product that were undoubtedly due to a small amount of impurity.

In a continuation of the foregoing investigation, Devakul and Maarse (94) isolated from the gland liquid (known as "Meng Da" in Thailand) by gas chromatography the related compound *trans*-2-hexen-1-yl butyrate in addition to the major constituent (I).

As a result of these investigations, two closely related compounds *trans*-2-octen-1-yl acetate (III) and *trans*-2-decen-1-yl acetate (IV), isolated by distillation and gas chromatography from the steam distillates of *Rhoecocoris sulciventris* and *Biprorulus bibax*, respectively, are believed to be sex attractants (255).

$$CH_3(CH_2)_4CH{=}CHCH_2OCOCH_3 \qquad \text{(III)}$$

$$CH_3(CH_2)_6CH{=}CHCH_2OCOCH_3 \qquad \text{(IV)}$$

LEPIDOPTERA

Bombyx mori, silkworm moth

Butenandt (57, 58) obtained 1.5 grams of benzene extractive from 7000 virgin female abdominal tips. The active neutral fraction was esterified with succinic acid, and the ester was saponified and sublimed in a high vacuum at 60–70°. The 100 mg of impure, waxy, crystalline substance analyzed for carbon, hydrogen, and oxygen and was thought to be a diol of approximate composition $C_{16}H_{30}O_2$.

Working with an alcohol extract of 60,000 fertilized females, Makino et al. (227) obtained a neutral fraction which they passed through alumina to give 4.5 grams of orange wax. This was freed of sterols ("bombicestrol") to give a brown syrup that distilled at 100–110° (0.06 mm) as a thick, faintly yellow oil that elicited a circling dance in males at 0.0005 μg and caused wing vibration at 0.00025 μg. Chromatography of this oil on filter paper with butanol-acetic acid-water, 85% phenol, or benzene-methanol (6:4) as solvents showed spots at R_f 1.0, 0.98, and 0.82, respectively. The attractant, designated "bombixin," was obtained by elution of the spot from the paper; it showed 86.41% carbon and 12.05% hydrogen, did not absorb in the ultraviolet spectrum, and contained a primary hydroxyl group according to its infrared spectrum. The minute amount of material obtained was active at 2–4 $\times$ 10^{-5} μg.

Although Hecker (162) reported in 1956 that the pure 4-(*p*-nitrophenylazo)-benzoate of the attractant had been obtained from an extract of 313,000 female abdominal glands, saponification of this ester gave a substance showing activity at "below 10^{-5} μg/ml," which was considerably lower than that finally determined (10^{-12} μg/ml) for pure bombykol (65) by Butenandt and Hecker in 1961. The attractant was proposed as a doubly conjugated alcohol of 12–15 carbon atoms (162).

Using a petroleum ether extract of the sacculi laterales from 3428 females, Amin (14) obtained 13.5 mg of a p,p'-nitrophenylazobenzoate, m.p. 78°, that gave, on hydrolysis, a solution highly attractive to male moths. On the basis of a mixed melting point determination with N,N-dimethyl-p,p'-nitrophenylbenzamide, Amin decided that the silkworm moth sex attractant was dimethylamine. This was vigorously denied by Butenandt and Hecker (64), who showed that the minimum active concentration of dimethylamine was 10 mg/ml, whereas the natural attractant was many times more attractive to males.

In 1959, the pure attractant, designated "bombykol," was obtained as its 4'-nitroazobenzenecarboxylic acid ester and identified as 10,12-hexadecadien-1-ol (V) (59a, 60, 62). The extract prepared from 500,000 virgin female abdominal tips with ethanol-ether (3:1) was saponified, and the active neutral fraction was freed of sterols and esterified with succinic anhydride; saponification of the succinates, treatment with 4'-nitroazobenzenecarboxylic acid chloride, and chromatography gave 12 mg of the attractant derivative from which structure V was regenerated by saponification (65a, 163, 164).

$$CH_3(CH_2)_2CH{=}CHCH{=}CH(CH_2)_8CH_2OH \qquad \text{(V)}$$

Although the configuration of the conjugation in bombykol was at first thought to be *cis,trans* (62), subsequent synthesis of the four possible geometrical isomers of structure V showed bombykol to possess the *trans*-10,*cis*-12 form (61, 66, 165, 334).

Although Anders and Bayer (20, 37), as a result of an independent investigation of the gas chromatography of the female silkworm extract, reported the presence of three materials attractive to males, only one of these was highly active. Schneider and Hecker (296) had previously shown that several unsaturated alcohols were attractive to males in varying degree, but the most potent of these was only 10^{-6} times as strong as the natural attractant.

Oleic, linoleic, and 14-methyl-9,12-pentadecadienoic acids were isolated by Butenandt et al. (68) in 1963 from the female attractant glands.

Euproctis chrysorrhoea, gold-tail moth

Females (8000) were placed in containers connected to 4-liter flasks containing a drying agent and connected to several glass tubes filled with glass rings (to give a larger surface area); the flasks were immersed in Dewar cold flasks containing liquid air. The connecting glass tubes led to an uncooled tube filled with charcoal, and finally to an oil pump providing 2.5 cubic meters of air per hour. The pump was operated for 16 hours per day from July 2 to July 24. The first tube contained most of the water unabsorbed by the drying tube. The middle tube contained 100 ml of a mobile liquid readily soluble in petroleum ether and probably containing some 2-hexenal. Inhoffen (175) concluded that the attractant must be a gas at 20°C, condensing at —5° to a stable liquid.

Lasiocampa quercus, oak eggar moth

The female scent was collected by passing filtered air over the females and then into a U-tube immersed in liquid oxygen (203). It was sealed and stored in nitrogen.

Pectinophora gossypiella, pink bollworm moth

Extraction of 1000 female abdominal tips with methylene chloride gave approximately 30 mg of crude attractant. Attempts to purify the whole-moth extract by dissolving the extract in acetone and freezing the impurities at —15° were unsuccessful, although large amounts of sterols and triglycerides could be removed in this manner. Active preparations could also be obtained by steam distillation, although some attractant was not carried over by this procedure. Some purification of the extract was obtained by chromatography on a column of silicic acid, followed by thin-layer chromatography on the same adsorbent or on aluminum oxide. Gas chromatography of material thus purified showed several components to be present, only one of which showed activity on males when it emerged from the instrument; this active component may be an 18-carbon ester, according to comparisons of its retention time with those of several known esters. The extract is completely inactivated by boiling with acid or alkali or by treatment with bromine in carbon tetrachloride, but activity is retained after treatment with bisulfite solution (38).

Plodia interpunctella, Indian meal moth

Barth (28) concluded that the sex attractant must be highly volatile, since the production gland turned black on treatment with osmium-containing reagent, and must have the nature of an ethereal oil; it has no odor perceptible to humans.

Porthetria dispar, gypsy moth

According to Collins and Potts (82), chemical studies on extracts of the female abdominal tips were initiated in 1925 by Bloor, who concluded that the attractant was a relatively stable unsaponifiable substance soluble in fat solvents and slightly soluble in water. Fiske in 1926 suspected that the substance was an aldehyde but failed to isolate it, and the following year Souther concluded that the attractant was a saturated fat, protein, or ester that was destroyed by acid or base and continuously generated by the female through hydrolysis of a more complex compound.

In 1937, Prüffer (263) determined that 85% ethyl alcohol was the best solvent for extraction of the attractant from the females or their abdomens. Allowing the females to steep in the solvent for up to 12 hours gave a very active extract, whereas steeping for 24 hours gave a weaker extract, possibly due to extracting out inactive, masking substances. Extracts stored in glass-stoppered containers in the dark remained attractive for at least 3 years, whereas activity was lost after 1 year's storage in the light, the extract turning from a yellow to a grey-brown color.

Extracts prepared by von Zehmen (368) in 1942 using petroleum ether, 95–100% ethyl alcohol, chloroform, acetone, and ether were all active, but a carbon tetrachloride extract was unattractive to males. Males were attracted to loosely corked flasks containing the petroleum ether extract, as well as to the pants' pockets of a forester who had carried such flasks in his pockets. Ether extracts were pale green in color, whereas extracts prepared with other solvents were colorless. Removal of the solvents from all extracts left a substance with a cucumberlike odor.

In 1942, Haller et al. (154) reported that benzene was probably the solvent of choice for obtaining attractive extracts from the female abdominal tips. Attractiveness of the extract was markedly increased by hydrogenation (6). The attractant, residing in the neutral fraction of the extract, reacted with phthalic anhydride, from which it could be recovered by saponification. Attractant obtained in this way was designated "gyptol" by Acree (3), who obtained considerable purification of this material and its ester derivatives by successive column chromatography on magnesium carbonate and magnesium oxide (4, 5). Acree concluded that the activity of the gypsy moth sex attractant could be attributed to two, or possibly three, fatty esters derived from at least two different alcohols.

Stefanović (321, 322), working with a hydrogenated benzene extract of 500,000 female tips, obtained by steam distillation a highly attractive fluorescent, yellow oil with a characteristic odor. This oil was separated into 246 fractions, 19 of which were attractive in field tests. These 19 fractions were combined to give 100 mg of yellow-red oil.

After 30 years of study, chemists of the U. S. Department

of Agriculture isolated, characterized, and synthesized the sex attractant in 1960 (188). To isolate the attractant, it was necessary to clip the last two abdominal segments of many virgin female moths, separate the neutral fraction from a benzene extract of the tips, and either chromatograph by a tedious process on adsorbent columns or, what was more satisfactory, dissolve the neutral fraction in acetone, precipitate out the inactive solids, and subject the attractive yellow oil to paper chromatography. Of the five spots obtained, only one was attractive to males, and this was separated into a highly attractive colorless liquid (the major attractant) and a solid of much lower activity. A total of 20 mg of pure major attractant and 3.4 mg of minor attractant was isolated from 500,000 females. The structure of the major attractant was determined by degradation and other chemical studies, as well as by synthesis, to be d-10-acetoxy-cis-7-hexadecen-1-ol (VI) (188, 189).

$$
\overset{\text{c}}{\underset{\underset{\underset{\text{O}}{\parallel}}{\underset{\text{OCCH}_3}{|}}}{\text{CH}_3(\text{CH}_2)_5\text{CHCH}_2\text{CH}{=}\text{CH}(\text{CH}_2)_5\text{CH}_2\text{OH}}}
$$

(VI)

Porthetria monacha, nun moth

Extracts were prepared of the virgin females with petroleum ether, ether, acetone, chloroform, and 95–100% ethyl alcohol. The odor of the solvents did not mask the attractiveness of the extracts in the field (368). Extracts of the females and their abdomens prepared with 85% ethyl alcohol or xylene were very attractive in field traps, but xylene extracts became inactive during one year's storage in the dark at room temperature, whereas alcohol extracts lost none of their activity during this period (13).

Prodenia litura, Egyptian cotton leafworm

Flaschenträger (123, 124) found that isolated abdominal segments of virgin females lost their attractiveness in a vacuum but again became attractive to males within a short time after removal from an evacuated atmosphere. The attractant could be collected by extraction of the abdominal segments with purified ether, or by freezing it out in a stream of air followed by steam distillation and extraction with various solvents.

In 1963, Zayed et al. (367) homogenized and lyophilized the abdominal tips from 23,000 females and then extracted them with ethanol-ether (3:1). The unsaponifiable neutral fraction of this extract was freed of carbonyl-containing compounds and sterols and treated with succinic anhydride; the resulting half ester was saponified to give an alcohol that was treated with 4'-nitroazobenzene-carboxylic acid chloride. The resulting ester was extracted with acetone, and saponification of the 100 mg of acetone-soluble portion gave a substance attractive to males at 10^{-5} μg/ml. The attractant, which has not yet been identified, is probably an alcohol.

Synanthedon pictipes, **lesser peach tree borer**

The attractive substance could be removed from the female abdominal segments by gently wiping them with a wad of cotton, or by extracting them with ethyl alcohol but not with benzene, methylene chloride, ether, hexane, or distilled water. Abdominal segments wiped with cotton were no longer attractive, whereas the cotton was highly attractive to males (81a).

Tineola biselliella, **webbing clothes moth**

A crude petroleum ether extract of filter papers over which females had crawled remained attractive to males during refrigeration for one year. Active extracts could also be prepared from shark-skin filter paper sheets or combed unspun wool exposed to virgin females in mason jars; the filtered extract, concentrated at 70°, remained attractive for more than one year. A petroleum ether extract of 1000 females was freed of solvent to give a thick yellow oil which was then extracted with ether; a dilution of the ether extract to 1:500,000 still induced males to court (282).

Trichoplusia ni, **cabbage looper**

A methylene chloride extract of virgin female tips was subjected to gas chromatography. A strong peak, having a retention time midway between those of methyl laurate and methyl myristate was highly attractive to males, indicating that the attractant is fairly volatile and has a relatively low molecular weight. No corresponding peak could be found on gas chromatograms of extracts of male abdominal tips (173).

COLEOPTERA

Agriotes ferrugineipennis, **click beetle**
Ctenicera destructor, **click beetle**
Ctenicera sylvatica, **click beetle**

Paper chromatography of crude ether extracts of the female abdomens with ethanol-ammonia (95:5) as solvent gave active spots at R_f 0.93 for *A. ferrugineipennis,* 0.86 for *C. destructor,* and 0.88 for *C. sylvatica* (225a).

Ips confusus

By means of a vacuum pump, air was drawn through a box containing male-infested ponderosa pine log sections at 20 liters/min. The air then passed through a series of two freezing traps, the first at $-4°$ and the second at $-70°$. The thawed contents of both cold traps were highly attractive to the insects in field olfactometers. The attractive substance could be extracted from its aqueous emulsion by the use of petroleum ether and concentrated by distillation of the solvent at $80°$; the colorless oil obtained did not lose activity during storage under refrigeration for several weeks, but it became inactive through prolonged exposure to temperatures above $85°$ (341).

Limonius californicus, sugar beet wireworm

Paper chromatography of a crude ethyl alcohol extractive of the female abdomens with $0.1N$ ammonium hydroxide or ethanol-ammonia (95:5) as solvents gave spots at R_f 0.9 and 0.85 (or 0.82), respectively, that were attractive to males in laboratory tests. The attractant is quite stable at room temperature (225, 225a).

HYMENOPTERA

Bombus terrestris, bumblebee

The swarming attractant was obtained from male mandibular glands by extracting the male heads with pentane. The extract was subjected to thin-layer chromatography on silica gel with petroleum ether-ether (1:1) as solvent; spraying the plates with antimony pentachloride solution showed the attractant as a brown spot (R_f 0.45) with an ultraviolet absorption maximum at 260 mμ. The attractant was identified as farnesol (324, 325).

Diprion similis, introduced pine sawfly

In 1960, Coppel and his co-workers (83) reported that an attempt to trap the attractant by passing air rapidly over virgin females and then through various solvents was unsuccessful. The crude attractant was obtained by extracting crushed whole females with acetone or benzene and by rinsing, with ether, glassware that had contained the live or dead females. Ether extracts of filter paper that had been exposed to virgin females were also attractive to males, although the activity of several extracts was masked by unknown materials until these were removed by column chromatography (77). Considerable purification of the attractant was obtained on columns of Florisil or silicic acid, but not on alumina. An aliquot of material thus purified, weighing 0.02 μg, attracted males within 30 seconds in the field; within 5 minutes 500–1000 males were attracted from distances up to 100–200 feet. The attractant appears to be a saturated ester that may contain a free hydroxyl group.

Euglossa spp., bee

Flowers of *Castasetum, Cycnoches,* and *Stanhopea* orchids are free of nectar but contain plasma-rich labellar epithelium that attracts male *Euglossa* bees. The bees do not feed on this so-called nutritive tissue but remove a nutritious substance from the flowers. The epithelium is thus a pheromone-producing gland whose secretion is a mixture of up to 12 terpenoids. Thin-layer chromatography of this secretion from *Stanhopea tigrina* with chloroform-ether gave spots of R_f 0.0, 0.18, 0.34, 0.46, and 0.75 after treatment of the plates with antimony trichloride solution. The highly excited state of the attracted bees indicates that a constituent of the secretion may be a sex attractant. Female *Euglossa* are not attracted by the odor (343).

DIPTERA

Apis mellifera, honey bee

By means of gas chromatography of ether and ethanol extracts of queen bee heads, Callow et al. (74a) were able to identify in these extracts, besides *trans*-9-oxodec-2-enoic acid ("queen substance"), methyl 9-oxodecanoate, methyl 9-oxodec-2-enoate, methyl 9-hydroxydecanoate, methyl 9-hydroxydec-2-enoate, methyl *p*-hydroxybenzoate, nonanoic acid, decanoic acid, 2-decenoic acid, 9-oxodecanoic acid, 9-hydroxydecanoic acid, 9-hydroxydec-2-enoic acid, 10-hydroxydec-2-enoic acid, and *p*-methoxybenzoic acid; 18 other substances could not be identified. In contrast with the findings of Pain et al. (253), no evidence was found of azelaic, phenylacetic, or phenylpropionic acids. Of these substances, only "queen substance" was attractive to drones (72a).

Musca domestica, house fly

The excitant may be extracted from female flies with benzene, water, or ethyl alcohol. It is removed from aqueous solutions with benzene, but water cannot remove it from benzene solutions (278).

CHAPTER TEN

SYNTHESIS OF SEX ATTRACTANTS
AND RELATED STRUCTURES

American Cockroach (*Periplaneta americana*)

After the structure (2,2-dimethyl-3-isopropylidenecyclopropyl propionate) (VII) was proposed for the sex attractant of this insect, numerous attempts to synthesize it were made by several groups. Foremost among these groups was that in the Pesticide Chemicals Research Branch of the U. S. Department of Agriculture, several of whose members formed the team that isolated the attractant (190). A start was made by synthesizing the saturated structure (VIII) formed by catalytic hydrogenation of structure VII.

(VII)   (VIII)

Structure VIII, completely unattractive to male American cockroaches, appeared to be a mixture, since its gas chromatograms showed several peaks (186); identical chromatograms were obtained with hydrogenated VII.

Structure VII was finally independently synthesized very recently by two groups (86a, 187a, 345a). It was found to be unattractive to male American cockroaches and is therefore not the sex attractant, whose structure remains to be determined.

Silkworm Moth (*Bombyx mori*)

During their investigations into the nature of the sex attractant of the female silkworm moth, Butenandt and his co-workers (59) had ascertained the fact that the attractant was an alcohol containing two conjugated double bonds. As a consequence, they bioassayed for attractiveness several hundred synthetic substances, including unsaturated aliphatic and alicyclic alcohols (59, 162). It had already been shown (59) that a steam distillate of mulberry leaves, the natural food of silkworm larvae and known to contain 2-hexenal, evoked a weak sexual response in the adult male following its reduction to 2-hexenol with lithium aluminum hydride. A synthetic sample of 2-hexenol was attractive at 4 mg/ml. Increasing the carbon chain and number of double bonds increased attractiveness, 2,4-hexadienol (sorbyl alcohol) and 2,4,6-octatrienol being active at 0.1 and 0.001 mg/ml, respectively (59); cycloheptanone was active at 0.1 mg/ml. However, these three compounds caused wing flutter in females as well as males (162). The four possible geometrical (*cis-trans*) isomers of sorbyl alcohol were synthesized (67) and found to show no observable difference in attractiveness (162).

The natural sex attractant, identified in 1959 (62, 164) as 10,12-hexadecadien-1-ol (IX), was at first thought to have the *cis*-10,*trans*-12 configuration, but this became highly improbable when synthetic IX (70), prepared in the same year and found to be a mixture of the *trans,trans* and *cis,trans* isomers, showed a minimum activity level of 10^{-2} μg/ml as contrasted with 10^{-10} μg/ml for the natural product.

$$CH_3(CH_2)_2CH=CHCH=CH(CH_2)_8CH_2OH \qquad \text{(IX)}$$

Nevertheless, the natural and synthetic preparations showed the same physical constants. Mixtures of other *cis,trans* isomers of IX were also prepared synthetically (70).

Subsequent synthesis of the pure geometrical isomers of IX showed that the natural isomer (bombykol) possessed the *trans*-10,*cis*-12 form. These pure isomers were prepared simultaneously

TABLE 4.   COMPARATIVE ATTRACTANCY OF BOMBYKOL
AND ITS SYNTHETIC ISOMERS TO MALE
Bombyx mori.

Isomer	Attractancy (μg./ml.)		
	Ref. 334	Ref. 65	Ref. 66
cis-10,*cis*-12	—	1	1
cis-10,*trans*-12	10^{-5}	10^{-3}	10^{-2}
trans-10,*cis*-12	10^{-13}	10^{-12}	10^{-12}
trans-10,*trans*-12	100	10	100
Bombykol (natural)	10^{-10}	10^{-10}	10^{-10}

through independent procedures by teams of chemists at the Max-Planck-Institute of Biochemistry in Munich (65, 65a, 66, 165, 212) and at Farbenfabriken Bayer AG in Leverkusen (334). The comparative attractancy of bombykol and its synthetic isomers to male silkworm moths, as reported by these teams, is shown in Table 4. There seems to be no doubt from these results that the natural attractant is mainly the *trans*-10,*cis*-12 form, although the fact that its potency is 1000 times lower than that of the synthetically prepared material having this structure casts doubt on the absolute purity of the natural form. Investigators from both teams combined talents to prepare and patent (336, 337) the following compounds, whose attractiveness (μg/ml) to males is given: *trans*-10,*cis*-12-tetradecadien-1-ol, 100; *trans*-10.*cis*-12-hexadecadien-1-ol, 10^{-13}; *trans*-10,*cis*-12-octadecadien-1-ol, 10^{-6}.

Butenandt et al. (63) have patented the use, alone or mixed with insecticide, of the following unsaturated alcohols as insect attractants: 6,8-tetradecadien-1-ol, 5,7-tetradecadien-1-ol, 6,8-pentadecadien-1-ol, 10,12-pentadecadien-1-ol, 9,11-hexadecadien-1-ol, 10,12-hexadecadien-1-ol, 11,13-hexadecadien-1-ol.

Guex et al. (150) have patented the preparation of the *cis,cis* forms of 5,8-tetradecadien-1-ol (b.p. 100–107°/0.1 mm), 10,13-hexadecadien-1-ol (b.p. 105–109°/0.1 mm), and 9,12-hexadecadien-1-ol (bp. 101–105°/0.05 mm). Alkaline isomerization of these compounds caused conjugation to give mixtures of *trans*-6,*cis*-8- and *cis*-5,*trans*-7-tetradecadien-1-ol (b.p. 96–99°/0.1 mm), *cis*-10,*trans*-12- and *trans*-11,*cis*-13-hexadecadien-1-ol (b.p. 108–113°/0.15

mm), and *cis*-9,*trans*-11- and *trans*-10,*cis*-12-hexadecadien-1-ol (b.p. 112–116°/0.2 mm), respectively, as colorless oils useful as insect attractants.

Truscheit and Eiter (335) have patented the preparation of the following alcohols useful as insect attractants: *trans*-10,*trans*-12-tetradecadien-1-ol, *cis*-10,*trans*-12-tetradecadien-1-ol, 10,12,14-hexadecatrien-1-ol, 11-(2,6,6-trimethyl-1-cyclohexen-1-yl)-10-undecen-1-ol, 13,17-dimethyl-10,12,16-octadecatrien-1-ol, and a mixture of 10,12-tetradecadien-1-ol and 11-methyl-10,12-tridecadien-1-ol.

Farbenfabriken Bayer AG (118) has patented the preparation of various 10,12-hexadecadiene derivatives.

Butenandt et al. (68) have reported that 1,10-octadecanediol (prepared by lithium aluminum hydride reduction of 10-ketostearic acid), a mixture of palmityl and stearyl alcohols, and oleyl, linoleyl, and linolenyl alcohols (prepared by reduction of the corresponding acids), are all unattractive to male *Bombyx*, showing an attractancy level of at least 10 μg/ml.

It is of interest to note that a mixture of the *trans,trans* and *cis,trans* forms of 10,12-hexadecadien-1-ol is reported (264) to show strong anticatabolic activity in rats. Oral administration of the *trans, cis* and especially the *cis,trans* forms caused a weight increase in rats kept on a protein-deficient diet. The *cis,trans* form, at 1–1000 μg/kg, showed anticatabolic activity which is only caused by anabolic steroids in much higher doses. No androgenic or estrogenic effect was caused by the isomers at doses above 1 mg/kg. The compound (isomer not given) inhibits ovarian atrophy of old female rats, and it is nontoxic to these animals; the L.D.$_{50}$ (intraperitoneal) is 6.5 grams/kg.

The attractive power of 10,12-hexadecadien-1-ol prompted Buchta and Fuchs (53) to synthesize 10,13-diketo- and 7,10,13-triketohexadecanoic acids, methyl 10,13-dihydroxyhexadecanoate, and 1,10,13-hexadecanetriol. The attractiveness of these compounds has not yet been reported.

Riemschneider and Kasang (274) synthesized *cis*-10,*cis*-12- and *trans*-10,*trans*-12-heptadecadien-1-ol, which attracted male silkworm moths at concentrations of 1 and 10 μg/ml, respectively. Attempts to isomerize one of the *cis* double bonds to the *trans* form, in order to increase attractiveness, were unsuccessful. The *cis,cis* isomer lost none of its activity on storage for two years as long as it was protected from air and light. 10,12-Docosadien-1,22-diol and other unidentified primary and secondary conjugated diols were unattractive to males.

Gypsy Moth (*Porthetria dispar*)

For a number of years before the isolation and identification of the natural sex attractant, a total of several thousand organic substances were tested in the field for attractiveness to males. One of these, a commercially available formulation consisting of 11% 1,2-epoxytetradecane, 60% 1,2-epoxyhexadecane (X), 22% 1,2-epoxyoctadecane, 2% 1,2-epoxyeicosane, and 5% hydroxylic compounds (including a small amount of 1,2-hexadecanediol (XI) and one of its monoacetates) was particularly attractive, 0.25 gram luring a total of 50 males in a 3-week period during which 12 female abdominal tips lured 94 males (179). This formulation was also attractive to field-collected males in the laboratory but its activity was uncertain when tested on laboratory-reared moths because their sexual responses were very erratic (44). Following fractionation of the formulation, only structure X and the hydroxylic fraction were attractive in both laboratory and field tests. Although the natural extract placed in the field began to attract males promptly, the synthetic formulation was attractive only after an induction period of several days. Further investigation showed that while structure X is, per se, a fair attractant for the male moth, it slowly hydrolyzes with moisture during the induction period to produce structure XI, which is strongly attractive. The corresponding C_{14} and C_{18} diols were unattractive. The use of structures X (prepared

$$CH_3(CH_2)_{13}CH\underset{\diagdown\diagup}{\underset{O}{\quad}}CH_2 \xrightarrow{H_2O} CH_3(CH_2)_{13}CHOHCH_2OH$$

(X)   (XI)

in 60% yield by the peracetic acid oxidation of 1-hexadecene) and XI (prepared in 95% yield by the performic acid oxidation of 1-hexadecene) as male gypsy moth attractants has been patented (179).

In the first reported synthesis of a naturally occurring insect sex attractant, Jacobson et al. (188, 189) prepared the *dl*-form of 10-acetoxy-*cis*-7-hexadecen-1-ol (XIIa) in an overall yield of 0.2% (10 steps); it was identical in all respects save optical activity with the *d*-form. The *dl*-form was successfully resolved into the *d*- and *l*- forms by treating its acid succinate with *L*-brucine, separating the brucine salts by fractional crystallization from acetone, decomposing the salts, and saponifying the acid succinates with ethanolic alkali (183). All forms were equally attractive to male gypsy moths when tested in the field at 10^{-7} µg/trap. Hydrogenation of structure

XIIa to give 10-acetoxyhexadecanol caused a tremendous drop in activity; the saturated product attracted male moths in the field at 10^{-2} μg/trap (45, 189).

$$\overset{\text{c}}{CH_3(CH_2)_5CHCH_2CH = CH(CH_2)_n CH_2OH}$$

$$\underset{\underset{O}{\|}}{OCCH_3}$$

(XIIa) n = 5
(XIIb) n = 7 (gyplure)
(XIIc) n = 9

Truscheit et al. (338) have patented the preparation of 10-hydroxy-7-hexadecyn-1-oic acid as an intermediate in preparing the natural gypsy moth attractant.

Characterization of the natural gypsy moth attractant also resulted in the synthesis of a homolog, *d*-12-acetoxy-*cis*-9-octadecen-1-ol (XIIb), which has been designated "gyplure" (180, 191). This compound was prepared in high yield from ricinoleyl alcohol (available commercially from the reduction of ricinoleic acid, the major ingredient of castor oil) by acetylating both hydroxyl groups and then selectively saponifying the primary acetyl group with refluxing ethanolic potassium hydroxide.[1] Male gypsy moths in large numbers are lured to field traps containing as little as 10^{-5} μg of gyplure/trap, and the compound is attractive at 10^{-12} μg in laboratory bioassay tests (Table 5). Adlung (7) reported that 25 and 50 μg of the gyplure placed in field traps did not lure males until the traps had been out for 11 days.

The preparation and use of gyplure as a gypsy moth attractant have been patented (181, 182). The results of a 2-week test in the field are given in Table 6.

The *trans*-form of gyplure, prepared by elaidinization of the *cis* isomer with nitrous acid (191, 193), was inactive in both laboratory and field tests. It has been shown (Table 7) that a concentration of 20% or more crude *trans*-gyplure in formulations of *cis*-gyplure is sufficient to cause complete inactivation (184); the

[1] The secondary acetyl group is extremely resistant to saponification with ethanolic alkali, and it is necessary to use a diethylene glycol-potassium hydroxide mixture at 120° to break this linkage. This unusual stability appears to be due in some way to the position of the secondary acetyl group with respect to the double bond, since the same behavior was noted during the attempted saponification of the natural lure and of a higher homolog (*d*-14-acetoxy-*cis*-11-eicosen-1-ol (XIIc) (191).

TABLE 5.   COMPARATIVE ATTRACTANCY OF
GYPLURE AND ITS HOMOLOGS TO
MALE GYPSY MOTHS.

Compounds	Attractancy (μg)	
	Laboratory	Field
d-XIIa (natural)	10^{-12}	10^{-7}
dl-XIIa (synthetic)	10^{-12}	10^{-6}
l-XIIa (synthetic)	10^{-12}	10^{-6}
d-XIIa (synthetic)	10^{-12}	10^{-7}
d-XIIb (*cis*-gyplure)	10^{-12}	10^{-5}
d-XIIb (*trans*-gyplure)	10^{4}	2.5×10^{5}
d-XIIc	10^{-2}	10

TABLE 6.   RESULTS OF FIELD ATTRACTANCY
TESTS WITH GYPLURE AND NATURAL
LURE.

Chemical	Concentration (grams/trap)	No. of Male Moths Caught (15 days)
Gyplure	0.000025	555
	0.000010	503
	0.000005	588
	0.000002	415
Natural lure	(12 female tips)	498
Blank	—	0

mechanism of this inactivation is not known. The propyl and butyl analogs of *cis*-gyplure were completely devoid of activity in field tests (191). These results show that a *cis* double bond and an acetoxy group are necessary for activity.

A number of laboratory and commercial samples of gyplure showed little or no activity in laboratory and field tests. By means of column and gas chromatographic methods, developed by Jones and Jacobson (192), it was shown that these samples contained only 30–39% *cis*-gyplure, being contaminated with varying amounts of the following compounds: stearyl, oleyl, and ricinoleyl alcohols,

TABLE 7. NUMBER OF MALE GYPSY MOTHS CAUGHT BY
cis-GYPLURE CONTAINING VARIOUS AMOUNTS
OF *trans*-GYPLURE (25µg/TRAP).

Sample No.	% *trans*	Moths Caught (2 hours)
639	0	19
640	1	15
641	3	14
642	5	22
643	10	13
644	15	25
645	20	4
646	30	0
647	40	0
648	50	0
649	100	0

oleyl acetate, ricinoleyl alcohol diester, 1-acetoxy-*cis*-9-octadecen-12-ol, and three unidentified substances. Each of these contaminants is completely devoid of attractiveness to gypsy moth males. In order to obtain a satisfactory grade of gyplure, it is necessary to use a pure grade of ricinoleyl alcohol and to have rigid control over production conditions. *cis*-Gyplure, free of all byproduct impurities (according to gas chromatograms), is highly attractive to males in the laboratory and in field traps. Contamination with as little as 7% (by weight) of ricinoleyl alcohol will completely mask activity, but ricinoleyl diacetate does not appear to affect activity (345b).

Stefanović et al. (320) reported the preparation of three samples of gyplure whose properties agreed closely with those given by Jacobson, except that the optical activity $[\alpha]_D^{20}$ was 18.86°, 19.54°, and 17.41°, respectively, as compared with $[\alpha]_D^{22}$ 10.12° for Jacobson's sample. None of Stefanović's samples was attractive to males, whereas Jacobson's sample was reported as being "slightly attractive" by Stefanović. No explanation was found for the difference in optical rotation.

Reduction of *d*-9-hydroxy-*cis*-12-octadecenoic acid, isolated from *Strophanthus kombe* seed oil, with lithium aluminum hydride gave *cis*-12-octadecene-1,9-diol, which was acetylated with acetyl chloride to the 1,9-diacetate; saponification with 1 mole of ethanolic potassium hydroxide gave d-9-acetoxy-cis-12-octadecen-1-ol (XIII). None of these compounds elicited a typical sexual response from male gypsy moths when tested in the laboratory (193).

$$CH_3(CH_2)_4CH\overset{c}{=}CH(CH_2)_2\underset{\underset{\displaystyle O}{\overset{\displaystyle \|}{\underset{\displaystyle}{OCCH_3}}}}{CH}(CH_2)_7CH_2OH \qquad \text{(XIII)}$$

Nun Moth (*Porthetria monacha*)

Trimethylamine, having an odor like that of the female nun moth, lures no males into field traps. Trials with "muscaro," musk, gum animé, civet paste, ambrette, "bear root," "pest root," and patchouli caught no males in one day; trapping of one male with civet was assumed to be accidental since one female in the same area lured 368 males during the same period (157).

Although gyplure lured male gypsy moths to field traps, 25 and 50 μg of this substance failed to lure male nun moths in an area infested with this insect (7).

Wireworm (*Limonius spp.*)

Lehman (222) tested approximately 150 chemical compounds in the laboratory for attractiveness to adult *L. canus* and *L. californicus*. Caproic, lactic, butyric, and valeric acids appeared to be sex attractants for males, eliciting a high degree of excitation, extension of the genitalia, and copulatory attempts. Caproic acid in field traps caught large numbers of males (2745), but only 1589 female *L. canus* were attracted to 32 traps; corresponding numbers for *L. californicus* were 8 and 10, respectively. Butyric acid in the field attracted 1589 male and 156 female *L. canus* in 34 traps, and only 5 male and 1 female *L. californicus*.

June Beetle (*Phyllophaga lanceolata*)

Isoamylamine produces a male response similar to that elicited by crushed or sexually active females. On a day with a strong wind, isoamylamine stimulated males to activity from as far away as 50–75 feet (333).

Honey Bee (*Apis mellifera*)

Investigation of the attractiveness of queen bees for the workers showed it to be due to a mixture of volatile acids with *trans*-9-oxodec-2-enoic acid ("queen substance"). An artificial mixture of phenylacetic, phenylpropionic, p-hydroxybenzoic, azelaic, and sebacic acids with "queen substance" did not produce attractivity. Similarly, mixtures of each of the following acids with "queen substance" failed to attract workers: *cis*-9-oxodec-2-enoic, *trans*-8-oxonon-2-enoic, *trans*-8-oxodec-2-enoic, *trans*-9-hydroxydec-2-enoic, 6-oxo-heptanoic, 7-oxooctanoic, 8-oxononanoic, 9-oxodecanoic, *trans*-2-nonene-1,9-dioic, *trans*-9-oxo-9-phenyldec-2-enoic, 9-oxo-2-decynoic (253).

Wild Bees

Kullenberg (214) found that male *Macropis labiata* respond to the following sex attractants, arranged in ascending order of effectiveness: methyl pelargonate, farnesal, undecalactone, nerolidol, farnesol (resembling the scent of the female). Only nerolidol and farnesol caused excitation, and the males could not distinguish with certainty between farnesol and the female scent at equal concentrations.

Farnesol and phenylethyl alcohol acted as sexual attractants and excitants for male *Bombus lapidarius*, while butyric and valeric acids repelled males (214).

Very extensive investigations of bumble bee sex attractants and excitants conducted by Kullenberg (215) showed most of the active substances to be mono- or sesquiterpene alcohols. Farnesol and nerolidol were the most effective excitants for male *Macropis labiata*; undecalactone was also attractive. The best imitation of the complex scent secreted by the female was undecalactone plus farnesol; this was very attractive to males on mating flights, even eliciting attempts at copulation.

Wasps (*Crabro cribrarius*)

Substances acting as sex attractants for males were allyl alcohol, benzaldehyde, rhodinol, geraniol, citronellol, nerolidol, farnesol, citronellal, hydroxycitronellal, and the scent from flowers of *Ophrys insectifera*. Citronellal, hydroxycitronellal, and the *Ophrys* scent also acted as excitants, as did farnesol and nerolidol occasionally. None of these substances evoked copulatory attempts. Allyl alcohol and benzaldehyde were not attractive at high concentrations, and capric and caprylic acids were repellent (214).

Citronellal was the most effective attractant and sexual excitant for *Crabro cribrarius* males, although isopulegol had some excitant effect. Butyric acid was both attractive and excitatory. Imitations of the female scent containing citronellal, nerolidol, and butyric acid, or citronellal plus nerolidol (imitation of the female abdominal scent), or nerolidol plus butyric acid (imitation of the cephalic scent) were also attractive (215).

Indian Water Bug (*Lethocerus indicus*)

Synthetic *trans*-2-hexen-1-yl acetate (b.p. 165–166°), identical in all respects with the substance produced by the male insect, may serve to excite the female immediately before or during mating (69), and the corresponding synthetic butyrate, identical with the natural material isolated from the gland liquid ("Meng Da"), may serve the same purpose (94).

CHAPTER ELEVEN

SEX ATTRACTANTS
IN INSECT SURVEY

The high specificity of the sex attractants has made them extremely valuable for detection and estimation of insect populations. The insect, in responding to a lure-baited trap, is caught and thereby signals the presence of its species. Thus a good attractant can assure the early detection of an infestation before it can enlarge or spread. Control measures need be applied only to those areas where the insect is found and only as long as it continues to be present. A good lure can accurately delineate an infestation and locate the last few, hard-to-find insects.

Gypsy Moth (*Porthetria dispar*)

The gypsy moth is an excellent example of an insect whose sex attractant may be used for survey and possibly for control. Males fly into the wind and pick up the scent as they approach the nonflying females (43).

A very complete history of the gypsy moth problem in Europe, Asia, Africa, and the United States is given by Schedl (287), who describes in detail the biology, life history, host plants, predators, and methods of survey and control for this insect. However, many detailed observations of male attraction by females had previously been given in 1896 by Forbush and Fernald (126), whose attempts to use traps baited with living virgin females for control proved to be unsuccessful, although many males were caught. Later the

104

same traps were found to be efficient detectors of moth infestations.

Early attempts to find the best type of gypsy moth trap involved the use of many types of paper or cardboard traps, baited with live virgin females or their crude extracts, which were tacked to the trunks of trees in and around infested areas (82, 171). Major advances were the findings that living females could be replaced by their last two abdominal segments and that an extract of these tips was similarly effective. Collins and Potts (82) described in 1932 the use of such materials from 1913 to 1931 to survey areas for infestation; their report contains many valuable detailed test results relative to type of traps, effective distance, and stability of the attractant.

In 1934, Jacentkovski (178) described tests conducted in Czechoslovakian wooded areas in which small matchboxes containing virgin female gypsy moths were tacked to tree trunks and surrounded by sticky fly paper strips. A total of ten such traps was set out and checked twice each day for male catches. Many males were caught on the papers during daylight hours, mainly at midday, and it was estimated that such males could be lured from a distance of approximately 100 meters. Empty containers that had previously held females remained effective for two or three days. This work was reviewed by Eckstein (104) in 1937.

Prüffer (263) tested the attractive power of many extracts, prepared from different parts of the female's body, which were contained in cloth bags hung on tree branches in a garden at distances of 0.5–1.0 meter apart; males released in the garden experienced no difficulty in locating active materials.

Komareck and Pfeffer (213) reported that they could verify the work of Jacentkovski (178) and that the method could be successfully used in the survey of areas for gypsy moth.

As a result of survey tests conducted over a period of several years with benzene extracts of virgin female gypsy moths and nun moths, Görnitz (137) reported that the gypsy moth extract lured many more male nun moths than male gypsy moths, whereas female nun moth extract lured almost exclusively male nun moths. However, Schwinck (302) reported that females of each species confined in small containers placed on glued boards lured equally males of either species in the field.

Although Görnitz (137) reported that a benzene extract of female gypsy moths lost little or no activity during storage at room temperature over a four-year period, Haller et al. (154) found that the abdominal tip extract deteriorated rapidly, so that most of its original potency was lost when it was exposed during the flight season one year later. The activity of the extract could be stabilized by prompt hydrogenation, followed by storage at 4°C (6, 154). Hydrogenated lures collected 9, 4, 3, 2, and 1 years previously proved to be equally effective in survey traps. Tests to determine the effect of lure concentration on male moth captures showed that concentration (tips per trap) paralleled captures but increasing the tip strength above 16 per trap did not result in significantly greater captures. Because of this finding, traps holding natural extract and used in the field for survey work were baited with 12–16 tips each. In 1957, the charge was further reduced to 12 tips per trap, because tests made each summer over a 7-year period failed to demonstrate any significant difference between traps containing charges equivalent to 12 and 16 tips (171).

Maksimović (228, 229) set forth the results of his investigations of the relation between number of gypsy moth egg clusters and the number of males caught in traps baited with the attractant extract. These tests, conducted in Yugoslavia, showed a ratio with a certain regularity. Traps baited with the equivalent of 12 female tips were most effective, catching males over a period of 1.5 months, so that such traps could be placed in and around infested areas immediately before the expected start of male flight. Female extract hydrogenated immediately following its preparation was somewhat more attractive than an extract hydrogenated after three months' storage.

Although Collins and Potts (82) reported that under certain conditions small numbers of male gypsy moths could be lured from as far as $2\frac{5}{16}$ miles, much more recent tests showed that the maximum effective distance of the lure was probably close to $\frac{1}{2}$ mile.

An excellent report by Holbrook et al. (171) in 1960 discussed in detail trap design and color, bait dispensers, duration of bait effectiveness, bait strength requirements, trap height and placement, and other investigations related to the gypsy moth trapping program. For many years, the U. S. Department of Agriculture made use of hydrogenated benzene extract of the abdominal tips in the metal (Graham) field traps, shown in Figure 7, to locate infested areas and to determine the size of the infestation by the numbers of males caught in these traps. The metal traps contained adhesive-coated (Tanglefoot) paper liners and rolled filter paper cartridges impregnated with lure. Males attracted to these traps flew in through a small round opening in the cardboard-cone ends and became entangled on the sticky surface of the liner. Although these metal traps were quite efficient, they had the following major disadvantages; they were (1) expensive, (2) laborious to clean after each season's use, and (3) bulky, requiring large amounts of storage space between flight seasons. The disposable, inexpensive cup-type paper trap (248) shown in Figure 8 has completely replaced the Graham trap, and synthetic gyplure, at a concentration of 25 μg per trap, is used exclusively as the attractant. These paper traps, containing gyplure impregnated on small dental-roll wicks and a Tanglefoot-coated liner, are hung on the limbs of trees; attracted males enter through an opening in each end of the cup. Each year, immediately before the male moth flight season (July–August), approximately 50,000 traps are placed in the infested New England area. The potency of gyplure is such that a single pound of the attractant, which may be made quite inexpensively, is sufficient to last for more than 300 years if used for survey alone (43).

Air movement is probably the most important consideration in trap placement (171). Traps situated upwind from an infestation are more apt to catch insects than those down or across wind. Traps placed in hollows or among dense growth do not catch well owing to restricted air movement. Odors of chemicals tend to sink to the ground because they are almost always heavier than air. The male gypsy moth apparently has adapted its behavior to this property since it flies long distances close to the ground. Catches of this moth in traps placed between ground level and 6 feet above showed little difference but fell off at the 12-foot level.

Nun Moth (*Porthetria monacha*)

The information given for the use of sex attractant in nun moth control (see Chapter 12) is pertinent for survey programs for this insect.

Pink Bollworm (*Pectinophora gossypiella*)

Preliminary tests by Ouye and Butt (251) and by Berger et al. (38), using 8-oz cup-type disposable gypsy moth traps lined with Tanglefoot showed that a crude extract of the female moth or its abdominal tips could be used in a field survey program. Although this trap used in cotton fields captured the males satisfactorily when the Tanglefoot was fresh, the Tanglefoot tended to harden and failed to hold moths after exposure to the air for 1 or 2 days; it also interfered with fluorescent dyes used to tag moths. Tests were then made with a modification of this trap, in which a portion of the bottom of a trap was replaced with

Figure 7. Graham field trap formerly used for luring male gypsy moths. [By permission of the U. S. Department of Agriculture.]

Figure 8. Cup-type gypsy moth trap in use today. [By permission of the U.S. Department of Agriculture.]

unbleached muslin; an aluminum foil container for calcium cyanide powder was taped immediately below the muslin (146). The cyanide gas released entered the trap through the muslin but kept the dead moths out of the powder. Later, a larger trap was constructed from sheet metal; its bait chamber was similar in design to the gypsy moth trap but a funnel connected to the bottom channelled the dead moths into a 1-quart cyanide jar. Each trap was baited with filter paper saturated with methylene chloride extract of 100 adult females at least 3 days old (146).

Oak Eggar Moth (*Lasiocampa quercus*)

Using caged females and marked males released from various distances, Dufay (97) determined that males could be lured from a distance of about 1 km, depending upon wind velocity and direction. The sex attractant could therefore be used to determine the size of field infestations.

Tobacco Hornworm Moth (*Protoparce sexta*)

Both sexes of the moth are attracted to black light traps. Hoffman (170a) found that placing cages containing virgin females of *Heliothis virescens*, *H. zea*, or *P. sexta* near such light traps increased the catch of male hornworm moths nearly sixfold.

Cabbage Looper (*Trichoplusia ni*)

Shorey and Gaston (313b) observed increased male responses to a visible light source during their studies with female extracts. Field and laboratory studies conducted by Henneberry and Howland (165a) showed that black light traps baited with 50 virgin female moths caught approximately twenty to thirty times as many males as were caught with light traps alone. A light trap without virgin females operated 20 feet from the baited trap caught ten to fifteen times as many males as did unbaited traps 1–2 miles away, indicating that the presence of virgin females in close proximity to a light source substantially influences the number of males caught. The number of females caught in light traps was not influenced by the presence of virgin females.

Lesser Peach Tree Borer (*Synanthedon pictipes*)

Cleveland and Murdock (81a), using sticky board traps baited with live virgin females, showed that males could be attracted from a distance of 500 feet. The traps consisted of pressed boards (6 × 8 inches), painted yellow and coated with Stickem (97% polymerized butene), bearing a centrally located hole into which was placed a 1 × 3-inch plastic screen cage holding a female. A total of 29 such traps kept in the field from May 10 to July 22 caught a total of 388 males on various days during this time. Attractive females each lured an average of 23 males.

Banded Cucumber Beetle (*Diabrotica balteata*)

Sticky board traps baited each with an attractive female and placed in a soybean field lured males within a short time (84). Traps baited with filter papers impregnated with extracts of female abdomens were set in a Latin square arrangement 9–12 feet apart in fields having high populations of the insect. During the first 24 hours, a 10-female equivalent of the extract was almost two and a half times as attractive as a virgin female, whereas a 1-female equivalent was about one-third as attractive. Lure was lost steadily by volatilization, so that by the third day the 10-female equivalent was only half as effective as a virgin female.

Dendroctonus pseudotsugae

The response of flying beetles to field olfactometers baited with logs infested with females exhibited a distinct diurnal and seasonal pattern which was influenced by several environmental factors; temperature was the most important. In the morning response flight began, as soon as a threshold temperature of 68°F was attained, and reached its peak around noon. Later in the season, high temperatures during midday always resulted in marked depression of flight. Beetles flew toward the infested logs against the wind, and the intensity of the wind limited their flight; beetles stopped flying when the wind reached a continuous velocity of more than 5 miles per hour. The ability of baited olfactometers to compete with naturally occurring attraction centers indicates their usefulness in survey (and possibly in control) of this bark beetle. The attractive substance from the frass can be concentrated and used under field conditions. The duration of the attraction can be artificially prolonged throughout the flight season, since females under field conditions cease production of the attractive substance after mating (284).

Ips confusus

Field attraction showed a definite diurnal pattern (8–10 A.M. and 2–6 P.M.). Beetles preferred the regions of least wind, but light conditions had little influence on response flights except that direct solar radiation seemed to be avoided. Beetles responded against the wind along an olfactory gradient. This distance over which populations may respond in colonizing new host material is estimated at 500–1000 meters (133).

Sugar-beet Wireworm (*Limonius californicus*)

Microscope slides moistened with a 70% ethanol extract of females and placed in an infested field attracted numerous males within 10 seconds from as far away as 40 feet. Males moved rapidly toward the slides, crawling and flying excitedly, and extruded their genitals repeatedly after reaching the slides. Males were attracted in a field that had no previously recorded history of infestation, showing that the crude extract can be used as a survey tool where population density is low (225).

Hessian Fly (*Phytophaga destructor*)

Cylindrical cages 1 inch in diameter and 3 inches tall containing 5 newly emerged virgin females were placed on the surface of the ground in a field. A larger wire cage 3 inches in diameter and 10 inches tall, painted with Tanglefoot, was placed around each small cage. A total of 5 cages exposed from April 2 to April 7 caught a total of 3627 males. The males advanced against the wind; the greatest numbers were found in cages up to 3 inches above the ground. The weather was clear and warm, with a wind velocity at 6–8 miles per hour from south to southwest (76).

CHAPTER TWELVE

SEX ATTRACTANTS
IN INSECT CONTROL

Lesser Wax Moth (*Achroea grisella*)

After Kunike (217) had determined that the male lesser wax moth secretes a substance which attracts and excites the female, he suggested that the material might be used to control this pest of bee hives. He felt that if the substance could be synthesized it might be placed in the vicinity of the hives, surrounded by glue, and used to lure large numbers of virgin females to their death. Failing this, a number of live males surrounded by glue could be placed in the vicinity of the hives with the same effect.

Nun Moth (*Porthetria monacha*)

In 1930–1931, a Czechoslovakian entomologist named Dyk fastened small containers of female nun moth pupae to tree trunks in infested areas and surrounded the containers with sticky flypaper strips. Females emerging in these containers lured large numbers of males (Figure 9), suggesting that this procedure could be used for control; this method became known as "Dyk's nun moth control" (224). It was tried in the same country in 1931 by Jacentkovski (177), who placed on a tree in a nun moth-infested forest a small matchbox containing a virgin female; 50 males were caught on the sticky strips during the first night of exposure. A total of 69 of these traps, baited with 85 virgin females during the period July 21 to August 14, caught 9662 males, despite the presence of predators. Each female remained attractive for approxi-

112

Figure 9. Male nun moths lured by live female. [From
O. Farsky, *Anz. Schädlingskunde,* 14, 52 (1938), Verlag
Paul Parey, Berlin.]

mately 8 days. Although Dyk was able to lure large numbers
of males to containers of females, he soon realized that control
by this means was impractical. Since the female's attractiveness
was strongest immediately after emergence and ceased with oviposition, and males were usually first to emerge, his idea was to collect
female pupae, allow the adults to emerge in a warm laboratory,
and expose these females in a male-infested area before normal
female emergence in the field (99).

In 1937, Ambros (10, 11) reviewed Dyk's method and decided
to try it, using cardboard matchboxes (10 × 15 cm) to hold his
females and the easily available sticky paper strips on tree trunks.

Female larvae and pupae were collected by school children 7–14 years of age and the larvae were reared to the pupal stage on pine twigs in open plots covered with gauze to prevent escape. Ambros reported that male catches were "spectacular," with traps tacked to the east or southeast side of trees catching best. Even traps that had previously contained a female for 24 hours remained attractive for three nights, but females held in place on the sticky strips fell prey to small animals and the strips did not catch well in rainy weather. It was found that large numbers of males could be caught before the main female emergence started, and Ambros felt that this method of control would be cheaper than using arsenic. This work was reviewed by Eckstein (104).

Elated by his previous results, Ambros (12) ran a large-scale trial (1916 square hectares) using five virgin females in each standardized cardboard trap. Traps were hung on trees 160 meters apart at a height of 1.5 meters from the ground and were surrounded by glue-covered paper sheets 12 cm wide and 60 cm to 1 meter long. A glue known as "Liparin," maufactured by a Czechoslovakian firm, was used, since it was not affected by rain, remained tacky for the entire flight period (59 days), and did not harden in cool weather. Placing a wad of cotton with the females in each trap increased the effective period for a few days after the females died (8–14 days). In order to insure a supply of females sufficient to last for the entire flight period, female pupae were collected, stored, and transported at 2°C, and warmed as needed; although the cold pupae became stiff and hard, warming caused the emergence of normal females. Traps (approximately 2 for each hectare) were checked each morning for male catch. To Ambros' surprise and delight, a total of 150,104 males were wiped out in this test! Most of the males flew in from the east against a westerly wind. The effective radius for these traps was not greater than 300 meters, as contrasted with 3.3–3.8 km reported previously by Collins and Potts (82) for gypsy moth traps. A total catch of 384,448 males in 49 days was reported by Ambros (13) in 1940 with 480 traps set in 756.57 square hectares. Results obtained with the natural attractant caused Ambros to doubt that an equally effective synthetic attractant for the nun moth could be found.

Modifications of Dyk's method were tried on a small scale by Hanno (157), utilizing gauze-covered cardboard containers of females. These containers were (1) tacked to a sticky oilpaper-covered board nailed to a tree trunk, (2) tacked to a large sheet of sticky paper nailed around a tree trunk, or (3) tacked to the tree trunk and surrounded by a wooden frame holding flypaper strips. During the period from July 14 to September 4, traps tested by method (3) in three sites caught only 18, 13, and 18 males, respectively, probably due to loss in tackiness of the strips from heat and winds; methods (1) and (2) proved to be more effective. A container of two live females set out July 19 by method (1) lured 204 males by July 22, when the females were removed; the empty trap then caught 59 males on July 23, 16 males on July 26, 1 male on July 28, and 3 males on August 8. Hanno could not substantiate Ambros' reports of best results with positions on the east or southeast side of trees, since this was dependent on wind direction. He was very optimistic about the possibility of using these trapping methods in both survey and control of nun moths, since one trapped male is prevented from fertilizing numerous females.

During the following year, Nolte (249) reported that Dyk's method of luring male nun moths with females surrounded by sticky papers was impractical for either survey or control of this insect, although it served to show the presence of the insects in an area and could cause male congregation. He tried Ambros' method using paper strips as well as square paste-covered boards, but the former were effective for only a short period and the latter were too expensive. Nolte found the method of Hanno best, using paste-covered oilpaper sheets wrapped around tree trunks; the female was placed in the center in a small paraffined cardboard container covered with gauze held in place with a rubberband. On trees with highly cracked bark, Nolte recommended the insertion of wrapping paper under the oiled paper to facilitate the application of paste. Each container should have at least two females, which should be renewed at least every five days. Trap sheets should be checked every day if possible, male counts made, and the paste renewed if necessary. Although Nolte found that captured males could be eaten by birds and mice, placing of the containers on the paste-covered sheets prevented ants from reaching the females. It was determined that placing a large number of traps in a given area did not affect the total number of males caught, since each trap then caught fewer numbers. Depending on the area used (Nolte surveyed nine areas in three years), traps caught a total from 239 to 3560 males. In any one night, the largest number of males caught in a trap was 578.

To determine the effective distance of the lure, 24 traps were set at various distances from a wooded area surrounded by a flat,

treeless terrain; one trap was set in the wooded area to indicate
the start of male flight. Each trap was provided with fresh females
daily. Flight began on July 21, 1938, and ended on August 22,
during which time a total of 11 males was caught in traps 100
meters away from the woods, 13 in traps at a distance of 200
meters, and none at 300–1000 meters. In 1939, Nolte ran a similar
test using males marked with lacquer and released downwind in
the afternoon from a distance up to 700 meters in all directions.
The results of this test were not definite, since a bad storm developed in the next day or two, but a total of 20 males was attracted
from 200 meters, 2 males from 250 meters, 1 from 500 meters,
2 from 600 meters, and 1 from 700 meters. Flight was considerably
affected by inclement weather and wind direction. Largest numbers
of males were lured from the east and southeast, since the prevailing
winds during flight were usually from the west and northwest. Trap
position was important, since traps set in a depression seldom caught
as well as those placed on flat ground. There was no correlation
between the number of females per hectare and the number of
males caught in the area, but flight numbers and the numbers
of males attracted paralleled one another.

A field test conducted by Nolte (249) to determine whether
the fertilization of wild females could be prevented by the use
of a large number of traps was unsuccessful, as a normal number
of fertile eggs was found the following January. Nolte concluded
that such a test can be successful only if the male is caught before
he can find a female, but that this is improbable, owing to the
searching flight pattern of the male. He decided that Hanno's
method is useful for survey only, and that Dyk's method cannot
possibly be used for prognosis, since the size of the infestation
is dependent on several factors and the total number of eggs laid
is much greater than the number of males caught in a given area.

Grape Berry Moth (*Clysia ambiguella*)
Grape Vine Moth (*Lobesia botrana*)
Götz (138, 139, 140), in 1939 and 1940, reported on field
tests conducted in the vineyards of Geisenheim and Rüdesheim,
Germany, with the purpose of determining whether the live females
of these insects could capture sufficient numbers of males to prevent
large-scale fertilization of females. Geisenheim traps, placed on posts
approximately 150-cm high, consisted of 8 wooden boards each
having one side covered with glued white paper and the other
side covered with glued black paper; in the angle formed by these
boards was a gauze-covered container with several females. In a

nearby vineyard trap-glasses containing grape marc wine to which had been added 10 ml of wine vinegar and 5 grams of sugar per half-liter were placed at 3-meter intervals for catch comparison. Although catches were dependent on weather and numbers and ages of females used, live females were approximately 38 times more attractive than the trap glasses. Females 1 day old were more attractive than those 2 days of age, smaller numbers of males being attracted by females 9–13 days old. The largest numbers of males were attracted from the south and smallest numbers from the north. One trap in which 5 female *Clysia* moths had been placed, 4 of which had died mysteriously, caught 6 males on the white side and 20 males on the black side on July 7, 1937; on July 8, 9, and 10 the numbers caught were 37 and 79, 26 and 51, and 18 and 24, respectively. A heavy rainfall on July 10 knocked down the trap. Whereas the total number of males caught by this single trap was 271, only 212 *Clysia* moths of both sexes (predominantly females) were caught in 83 glass traps during the corresponding period. The trial also showed the moths to be positively phototropic. A single six-boarded trap with alternate boards having two white papers and two black papers was baited with five 2-day-old *Clysia* females and placed 25 meters from the nearest vineyard; it attracted 250 males to the white sides and 90 males to the black sides.

Rüdesheim vineyards contained primarily *Lobesia*, since these prefer a dry climate and *Clysia* a damp climate. Traps (Figures 10a and 10b) with four wooden boards covered with white papers only were baited with 6 females, permitted to catch for 3 days, and then provided with an additional 11 fresh, 1-day-old females; by the following day these traps had caught ten times more males than they had the previous day. Boards facing west showed the least number of males and those facing north and east showed the most males. Other traps containing 14 females apiece were set up on a meadow surrounded on three sides by vineyards (the closest one was 20 meters away) and on the fourth side by a vegetable garden; a total of 1069 males were caught in one day, whereas 5 glass traps caught a total of 8 moths in this period. Boards facing west and north caught the least numbers of males in this test.

With both species of grape insects, flight occurred mainly during periods having temperatures of 11.7–14.6°C, low wind velocity, and a relative humidity greater than 80%; very few males were caught during cool weather (143, 144).

Götz concluded that the trapping method was practical for

(a)

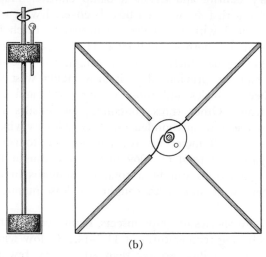

(b)

Figure 10. Four-winged field trap used for luring male *Clysia ambiguella*. (a) front view, (b) side and top views. [From B. Götz, *Anz. Schädlingskunde*, **15**, 109 (1939), Verlag Paul Parey, Berlin.]

control of these insects only if the attractant could be identified and synthesized.

The findings with regard to *L. botrana* were confirmed in field tests by Chaboussou and Carles (77a), using metal traps, and the same conclusions were reached regarding control of the insect by sex attraction. However, these authors found that equal numbers of males were attracted to black and to white traps baited with equal numbers of virgin females.

Gypsy Moth (*Porthetria dispar*)

In 1893, Kirkland (205) reported an unsuccessful attempt to use the attraction of females for males in gypsy moth control, although no details were given.

Beroza (39), in 1960, and Brown (52), in 1961, suggested that the control of gypsy moths by male confusion with gyplure might be successful, and in 1963, Babson (24) proposed that gyplure be broadcast by air over infested areas to confuse or frustrate the males during the mating period. In a reply, Burgess (55) pointed out that such a test had actually been undertaken by the Plant Pest Control Division of the U. S. Department of Agriculture during the summer of 1961. Gyplure, in both liquid and granular formulations, had been distributed by aircraft over Rattlesnake Island, a 400-acre island with varying intensities of gypsy moth infestation located in Lake Winnepesaukee, New Hampshire. Subsequent field observations revealed that the particular commercial gyplure used in this test had exhibited only weak attractiveness due to contaminant masking, and no adverse effect was obtained on male mating activity.

Plans were made to repeat the "confusion" test in the summer of 1964 with a large lot of laboratory-prepared gyplure (85% *cis* content) closely approximating that previously shown to be effective in both laboratory and field tests, but both granular (corn cob grits) and liquid (methylene chloride) formulations prepared especially for aerial application lured few males to field traps (345b). Intensive chemical and trapping investigations conducted during July and August of 1964 showed masking activity by 8% ricinoleyl alcohol. It was also found that an unidentified substance (or substances) present in technical grade, but not in reagent grade, methylene chloride masks, inhibits, or destroys the attractiveness of *cis*-gyplure.

Wright (363, 365b) theorized that insects can be controlled, at least in principle, by permeating the atmosphere with a sex attractant chemical so that the small additional quantity emanating from a female is imperceptible. He has coined the term "metarchon" (365c) for such an external stimulus artificially introduced into the environment of an organism for the purpose of modifying its behavior, by eliciting an inappropriate response or inhibiting an appropriate one. With gyplure, if the threshold concentration is taken as 10^3 molecules/mm^4 of scent, and it is assumed that a concentration 100,000 times higher than this will completely saturate or fatigue the male receptor organs, then the concentration required is 10^8 molecules/mm^4, and only 20 kg of gyplure would be required to saturate 600 km^4 of air. Wright's assumption that the air would not have to be permeated 100% of the time may not be valid, however, nor is his statement "insect strains 'resistant' to a sex attractant are not likely to arise" necessarily true (see reference 43 for a discussion of resistance to sex attractants in insects).

Nevertheless, the use of sex attractants in insect control, particularly for the Lepidoptera, is a definite possibility, as has been pointed out in reviews by Götz (145) and Beroza and Jacobson (43). Numerous males of certain species of moths can be lured to their deaths by the use of even crude extracts of the females placed advantageously in traps with insecticide or on sticky boards (184), and the use of a mixture of sex attractant and a chemical sterilant merits trial. Much greater damage to the insect population can be effected by insects rendered infertile by a chemosterilant than by outright killing of the insects. These chemosterilants could be exposed along with the attractants in dispensers that allow access only to the insect, for example, through small holes. Insects responding to the attractant could thus be brought in contact with the chemosterilant, or possibly be induced to feed on it by admixing it with the lure, and then be free to fly off and mate with normal individuals of the opposite sex; such matings would, of course, result in no progeny.

Introduced Pine Sawfly (*Diprion similis*)

The insect is a pest of eastern white pine in the United States. Since it was observed that large numbers of males swarmed toward females from the surrounding area, investigations were conducted to determine whether a male eradication program would be practical (83). The wooden traps used consisted of a board ($12 \times 6 \times 1$ inches) with a $2\frac{1}{2}$-inch screened opening in the center. A virgin female was placed in the screened portion and Tanglefoot was spread over the wooden portion. The traps were suspended from trees in infested areas. Traps baited with one virgin female attracted an average of 1000 males each (data from 8 traps), ranging from

542 to 1706; large numbers of uncounted males also fell to the ground. Some females did not attract males for an unknown reason. The male response was rapid, many approaching within 30 seconds after the traps were set up. Traps set up at an angle of 90 degrees to the wind direction at the edge of the woods were consistently more attractive than those set in the dense portion of the woods. Greatest activity took place from midmorning to midafternoon; no male movement was observed in the early evening hours before sunset. One trap with a virgin female exposed from 11 A.M. to 4 P.M. attracted more than 7000 males during this period; she continued attracting males at approximately 1000 per day until she died on the fifth day, after which small numbers were caught for the next 3 days. Males were lured 200 feet out of the forest over an open field.

Field control of the insect based on luring the males to an insecticide-attractant mixture seems unlikely. Chemosterilant-attractant mixtures should be more effective in reducing or eradicating a field population of this insect (77).

REFERENCES

1. Abbott, C. E. The physiology of insect senses. *Entomol. Americana*, **16**, 225 (1936).
2. Abbott, C. E. On the olfactory powers of *Megarhyssa lunator* (Hymenoptera: Ichneumonidae). *Entomol. News*, **47**, 263 (1936).
3. Acree, F., Jr. The isolation of gyptol, the sex attractant of the female gypsy moth. *J. Econ. Entomol.*, **46**, 313 (1953).
4. Acree, F., Jr. Studies on the chromatography of gyptyl azoate. *J. Econ. Entomol.*, **46**, 900 (1953).
5. Acree, F., Jr. The chromatography of gyptol and gyptyl esters. *J. Econ. Entomol.*, **47**, 321 (1954).
6. Acree, F., Jr., M. Beroza, R. F. Holbrook, and H. L. Haller. The stability of hydrogenated gypsy moth sex attractant. *J. Econ. Entomol.*, **52**, 82 (1959).
7. Adlung, K. G. Field tests on the attraction of male nun moths (*Lymantria monacha* L.) and gypsy moths (*Lymantria dispar* L.) to gyplure, a synthetic sex attractant. *Z. angew. Entomol.*, **54**, 304 (1964).
8. Allen, N., and C. R. Hodge. Mating habits of the tobacco hornworm. *J. Econ. Entomol.*, **48**, 526 (1955).
9. Allen, N., W. S. Kinard, and M. Jacobson. Procedure used to recover a sex attractant for the male tobacco hornworm. *J. Econ. Entomol.*, **55**, 347 (1962).
10. Ambros, W. Nonnenfalterkontrolle auf biologischer Grundlage. *Centr. ges. Forstwesen*, **63**, 140 (1937).
11. Ambros. W. Einige spezielle Beobachtungen und Untersuchungen während der Nonnenkontrolle im Jahre 1937. *Centr. ges. Forstwesen*, **64**, 49 (1938).
12. Ambros, W. Die biologische Nonnenfalterkontrolle 1937. *Centr. ges. Forstwesen*, **64**, 209 (1938).
13. Ambros, W. Einige Beobachtungen und Untersuchungen an der Nonne im Jahre 1938. *Centr. ges. Forstwesen*, **66**, 131, 166 (1940).
14. Amin, E. S. The sex-attractant of the silkworm moth (*Bombyx mori*). *J. Chem. Soc.*, **1957**, 3764.

15. Amoore, J. E. Elucidation of the stereochemical properties of the olfactory receptor sites. *Proc. Toilet Goods Assoc., Sci. Sect.,* No. 37, (Suppl.), 13 (1962).

16. Amoore, J. E. Stereochemical theory of olfaction. *Nature,* **198,** 271 (1963).

17. Amoore, J. E. Stereochemical theory of olfaction. *Nature,* **199,** 912 (1963).

18. Amoore, J. E. Current status of the steric theory of odor. *Ann. N. Y. Acad. Sci.,* **116,** 457 (1964).

19. Amoore, J. E., J. W. Johnston, Jr., and M. Rubin. The stereochemical theory of odor. *Sci. American,* **210** (2), 42 (1964).

20. Anders, F., and E. Bayer. Versuche mit dem Sexualduftstoff aus den Sacculi laterales vom Seidenspinner *(Bombyx mori* L.). *Biol. Zentr.,* **1959,** 584.

21. Anonymous. Love among the insects. *Time,* **79,** 66 (Oct. 11, 1963).

22. Anonymous. Operation cockroach. *Agr. Research* (*U. S.*), **12** (3), 8 (1964).

23. Antram, C. B. Sexual attraction in Lepidoptera. *J. Bombay Nat. Hist. Soc.,* **18,** 923 (1908).

24. Babson, A. L. Eradicating the gypsy moth. *Science,* **142,** 447 (1963).

25. Barnes, M. M., D. W. Robinson, and A. G. Forbes. Attractants for moths of the western grape leaf skeletonizer. *J. Econ. Entomol.,* **47,** 58 (1954).

26. Barrett, C. G. Lepidoptera on stone walls and rocks. *Entomol. Monthly Mag..* **22,** 111 (1886).

27. Barth, R. Bau und Funktion der Flügeldrüsen einiger Mikrolepidopteren. Untersuchungen an den Pyraliden *Aphomia gularis, Galleria mellonella, Plodia interpunctella, Ephestia elutella, E. kühniella.* *Z. wiss. Zool.,* **150,** 1 (1937).

28. Barth, R. Herkunft, Wirkung und Eigenschaften des weiblichen Sexualduftstoffes einiger Pyraliden. *Zool. Jahrb., Abt. Zool. Physiol. Tiere,* **58,** 297 (1937–1938).

29. Barth, R. Die männlichen Duftorgane einiger Argynnis-Arten. (Vergleichende Untersuchungen an *Argynnis paphia, Adippe* und *Aglaia*). *Zool. Jahrb., Abt. Anat. Ontog. Tiere,* **68,** 331 (1944).

30. Barth, R. Die Hautdrüsen des Männchens von *Opsiphanes invirae isagoras* Fruhst. (Lepidoptera, Brassolidae). *Zool. Jahrb., Abt. Anat. Ontog. Tiere,* **72,** 216 (1952).

31. Barth, R. Das männliche Duftorgan von *Erebus odoratus* L. (Lepidoptera, Noctuidae). *Zool. Jahrb., Abt. Anat. Ontog. Tierc,* **72,** 289 (1952).

32. Barth, R. H., Jr. Hormonal control of sex attractant production in the Cuban cockroach. *Science,* **133,** 1598 (1961).

33. Barth, R. H., Jr. Comparative and experimental studies on mating behavior in cockroaches. *Doctoral Thesis, Harvard Univ.,* 274 pp. (1961).

34. Barth, R. H., Jr. The endocrine control of mating behavior in the cockroach *Byrsotria fumigata* (Guérin). *Gen. Comp. Endocrinol.*, **2**, 53 (1962).

35. Barth, R. H., Jr. Endocrine-exocrine mediated behavior in insects. *Proc. XVIth Intern. Cong. Zool., Washington, D. C.*, **3**, 3 (1963).

36. Barth, R. H., Jr. The mating behavior of *Byrsotria fumigata* (Guérin) (Blattidae, Blaberinae). *Behaviour*, **23**, 1 (1964).

37. Bayer, E., and F. Anders. Biologische Objekte als Detektoren zur Gaschromatographie. *Naturwissenschaften*, **46**, 380 (1959).

37a. Benjamin, D. M. The biology and ecology of the red-headed pine sawfly. *U. S. Dept. Agr. Tech. Bull.*, no. **1118**, 57 pp. (1955).

38. Berger, R. S., J. M. McGough, D. F. Martin, and L. R. Ball. Some properties and the field evaluation of the pink bollworm sex attractant. *Ann. Entomol. Soc. Am.*, **57**, 606 (1964).

39. Beroza, M. Insect attractants are taking hold. *Agr. Chem.*, **15** (7). 37 (1960).

40. Beroza, M. Insect attractants. *Soap Chem. Specialties*, **36** (2), 74 (1960).

41. Beroza, M., and N. Green. Lures for insects. *Yearbook Agr. (U. S. Dept. Agr.)*, **1962**, 365.

42. Beroza, M., and N. Green. Synthetic chemicals as insect attractants. *Advances in Chem. Ser.*, no. **41**, 11 (1963).

43. Beroza, M., and M. Jacobson. Chemical insect attractants. *World Rev. Pest Control*, **2** (2), 36 (1963).

44. Block, B. C. Laboratory method for screening compounds as attractants to gypsy moth males. *J. Econ. Entomol.*, **53**, 172 (1960).

45. Block, B. C. Behavioral studies of the responses of gypsy moth males (*Porthetria dispar* L.) to the female sex attractant and related compounds. *Abstr. Eastern Branch Meeting Entomol. Soc. Am.* (Oct. 30, 1961).

45a. Bobb, M. L. Apparent loss of sex attractiveness by the female of the Virginia-pine sawfly, *Neodiprion pratti pratti. J. Econ. Entomol.*, **57**, 829 (1964).

46. Boch, R., and D. A. Shearer. Identification of geraniol as the active component in the Nassanoff pheromone of the honey bee. *Nature*, **194**, 704 (1962).

47. Boch, R., and D. A. Shearer. Production of geraniol by honey bees of various ages. *J. Insect Physiol.*, **9**, 431 (1963).

48. Boch, R., and D. A. Shearer. Identification of nerolic and geranic acids in the Nassanoff pheromone of the honey bee. *Nature*, **202**, 320 (1964).

49. Boeckh, J. Elektrophysiologische Untersuchungen an einzelnen Geruchsrezeptoren auf der Antenne des Totengräbers (Necrophorus, Coleoptera). *Verhandl. deut. Zool. Ges. Wien*, **1962**, 297.

50. Boeckh, J., E. Priesner, D. Schneider, and M. Jacobson. Olfactory receptor response to the cockroach sexual attractant. *Science*, **141**, 716 (1963).

51. Bornemissza, G. F. Sex attractant of male scorpion flies. *Nature*, **203**, 786 (1964).

51a. Bossert, W. H., and E. O. Wilson. The analysis of olfactory communication among animals. *J. Theoretical Biol.*, **5**, 443 (1963).

51b. Bounhiol, J. J. Physiologie de l'attraction sexuelle chez *Bombyx mori* (Lepidoptera). *Programme XIIth Intern. Cong. Entomol.*, *London*, **1964**, 68.

52. Brown, W. L., Jr. Mass insect control programs: four case histories. *Psyche*, **68**, 75 (1961).

53. Buchta, E., and F. Fuchs. 10.13-Dioxo- und 7.10.13-Trioxo-hexa-decansäure sowie 10. [13-Dihydroxy-hexadecansäuremethylester und Hexadecan-triol-(1.10.13). *Naturwissenschaften*, **48**, 454 (1961).

54. Burgess, E. D. Development of gypsy moth sex-attractant traps. *J. Econ. Entomol.*, **43**, 325 (1950).

55. Burgess, E. D. Gypsy moth control. *Science*, **143**, 526 (1964).

56. Burkhardt, D. Ultramikroelektroden aus Glas, ihre Herstellung und Verwendung bei elektrophysiologischen Messungen. *Glas-Instr.-Tech.*, **3**, 115 (1959).

57. Butenandt, A. Zur Kenntnis der Sexual-Lockstoffe bei Insekten. *Jahrb. preuss. Akad. Wiss.*, **1939**, 97.

58. Butenandt, A. Untersuchungen über Wirkstoffe aus dem Insekten-reich. *Angew. Chem.*, **54**, 89 (1941).

59. Butenandt, A. Über Wirkstoffe des Insektenreiches, II: Zur Kenntnis der Sexual-Lockstoffe. *Naturw. Rundschau*, **1955**, 457.

59a. Butenandt, A. Bombycol, the sex-attractive substance of the silk-worm, *Bombyx mori. J. Endocrinol.*, **27**, 9 (1963).

60. Butenandt, A., R. Beckmann, and E. Hecker. Über den Sexuallock-stoff des Seidenspinners, I: Der biologische Test und die Isolierung des reinen Sexuallockstoffes Bombykol. *Z. physiol. Chem, Hoppe-Seyler's*, **324**, 71 (1961).

61. Butenandt, A., R. Beckmann, and D. Stamm. Über den Sexuallock-stoff des Seidenspinners, II: Konstitution und Konfiguration des Bombykols. *Z. physiol. Chem., Hoppe-Seyler's*, **324**, 84 (1961).

62. Butenandt, A., R. Beckmann, D. Stamm, and E. Hecker. Über den Sexuallockstoff des Seidenspinners *Bombyx mori*. Reindarstellung und Konstitution. *Z. Naturforsch.*, **14b**, 283 (1959).

63. Butenandt, A., W. Guex, E. Hecker, R. Rüegg, and U. Schwieter. Insektenlockmittel. Ger. Patent 1,108,976 (June 15, 1961).

64. Butenandt, A., and E. Hecker. Dimethylamine, the supposed sex-attractant of the silkworm moth (*Bombyx mori*). *Proc. Chem. Soc.*, **1958**, 53.

65. Butenandt, A., and E. Hecker. Synthese des Bombykols, des Sexuallockstoffes des Seidenspinners, und seiner geometrischen Isomeren. *Angew. Chem.*, **73**, 349 (1961).

65a. Butenandt, A., and E. Hecker. La synthèse de bombycol. *Nucleus (Paris)*, **5**, 325 (1964).

66. Butenandt, A., E. Hecker, M. Hopp, and W. Koch. Über den Sexuallockstoff des Seidenspinners, IV: Die Synthese des Bombykols und der *cis-trans*-Isomeren Hexadecadien-(10,12)-ole-(1). *Ann.*, **658**, 39 (1962).

67. Butenandt, A., E. Hecker, and H. G. Zachau. Über die vier geometrischen Isomeren des 2,4-Hexadienols-(1). *Chem. Ber.*, **88**, 1185 (1955).

68. Butenandt, A., E. Hecker, and S. M. A. D. Zayed. Über den Sexuallockstoff des Seidenspinners, III: Ungesättigte Fettsäuren aus den Hinterleibsdrüsen (Sacculi laterales) des Seidenspinnerweibchens (*Bombyx mori* L.). *Z. physiol. Chem., Hoppe-Seyler's*, **333**, 114 (1963).

69. Butenandt, A., and N.-D. Tam. Über einen geschlechtsspezifischen Duftstoff der Wasserwanze *Belostoma indica* Vitalis (*Lethocerus indicus* Lep.). *Z. physiol. Chem., Hoppe-Seyler's*, **308**, 277 (1957).

70. Butenandt, A., E. Truscheit, K. Eiter, and E. Hecker. Verfahren zur Herstellung von Hexadecadien-(10,12)-ol-(1). Ger. Patent 1,096,345 (Jan. 5, 1961).

71. Butler, C. G. Pheromones in sexual processes in insects. *Insect Reproduction (Symposium No. 2, Roy. Entomol. Soc. London)*, **1964**, 66.

72. Butler, C. G., R. K. Callow, and J. R. Chapman. 9-Hydroxydec-*trans*-2-enoic acid, a pheromone stabilizing honeybee swarms. *Nature*, **201**, 733 (1964).

72a. Butler, C. G., and E. M. Fairey. Pheromones of the honeybee: biological studies of the mandibular gland secretion of the queen. *J. Apicult. Research*, **3**, 65 (1964).

73. Caillot, Y., and C. Boisson. Developpement larvaire du Belostome (*Lethocerus indicus* Lep.); Insecte Hemiptere, Hydrocoryse, Cryptocérate. *Ann. Sci. nat. Zool. et biol. animale*, [11], **16**, 51 (1954).

74. Callahan, P. S. A photographic analysis of moth flight behavior, with special reference to the theory for electromagnetic radiation as an attractance force between the sexes. *Programme XIIth Intern. Cong. Entomol., London*, **1964**, 48.

74a. Callow, R. K., J. R. Chapman, and P. N. Paton. Pheromones of the honeybee: chemical studies of the mandibular gland secretion of the queen. *J. Apicult. Research*, **3**, 77 (1964).

75. Campbell, W. H. Sexual attraction in Lepidoptera. *J. Bombay Nat. Hist. Soc.*, **18**, 511 (1908).

76. Cartwright, W. B. Sexual attraction of the female Hessian fly (*Phytophaga destructor* Say.). *Can. Entomologist*, **54**, 154 (1922).

77. Casida, J. E., H. C. Coppel, and T. Watanabe. Purification and potency of the sex attractant from the introduced pine sawfly, *Diprion similis. J. Econ. Entomol.*, **56**, 18 (1963).

77a. Chaboussou, F., and J. P. Carles. Observations sur le piégeage sexuel des males d'eudémis (*Lobesia botrana* Schiff.). *Rev. zool. agr.*, **61**, 81 (1962).

78. Champlain, A. B. The curious mating habit of *Megarhyssa atrata* (Fab.) (Hymen.: Ichneumonoidea). *Entomol. News*, **32**, 241 (1921).

79. Chapman, J. A. Evidence for a sex attractant in the elaterid beetle, *Hemicrepidius morio* (LeConte). *Can. Entomologist*, **96**, 909 (1964).

80. Chauvin, R. Étude du comportement des insectes. *Ann. biol.*, [4], **1**, 207 (1962).

81. Chen, S. H., and B. Young. Observations on the mating behavior of *Bombyx mori. Sinensia*, **14**, 45 (1943).

81a. Cleveland, M. L., and L. L. Murdock. Natural sex attractant of the lesser peach tree borer. *J. Econ. Entomol.*, **57**, 761 (1964).

82. Collins, C. W., and S. F. Potts. Attractants for the flying gipsy moths as an aid in locating new infestations. *U. S. Dept. Agr. Tech. Bull.*, no. **336**, 44 pp. (1932).

83. Coppel, H. C., J. E. Casida, and W. C. Dauterman. Evidence for a potent sex attractant in the introduced pine sawfly, *Diprion similis* (Hymenoptera: Diprionidae). *Ann. Entomol. Soc. Am.*, **53**, 510 (1960).

84. Cuthbert, F. P., Jr., and W. J. Reid, Jr. Studies of sex attractant of banded cucumber beetle. *J. Econ. Entomol.*, **57**, 247 (1964).

85. Dalla-Torre, K. W. v. Die Duftapparate der Schmetterlinge. *Kosmos*, **354**, 410 (1885).

86. Daniel, D. M. *Macrocentrus ancylivorus* Rohwer, a polyembryonic braconid parasite of the Oriental fruit moth. *N. Y. State Agr. Expt. Sta. Tech. Bull.*, no. **187**, 101 pp. (1932).

86a. Day, A. C., and M. C. Whiting. The structure of the sex attractant of the American cockroach. *Proc. Chem. Soc.*, **1964**, 368.

87. Deegener, P. Das Duftorgan von *Hepialus hectus*. *Z. wiss. Zool.*, **71**, 276 (1902).

88. Deegener, P. Das Duftorgan von *Phassus schamyl* Chr. *Z. wiss. Zool.*, **78**, 245 (1904).

89. Delmas, R. Notes sur la biologie de *Pristiphora conjugata*. *Bull. biol. France et Belg.*, **60**, 447 (1926).

90. Dethier, V. G. *Chemical Insect Attractants and Repellents*, Blakiston, Philadelphia, 1947, pp. 21–25.

91. Dethier, V. G. The physiology of olfaction in insects. *Ann. N. Y. Acad. Sci.*, **58**, 139 (1954).

92. Dethier, V. G., *The Physiology of Insect Senses,* John Wiley and Sons, New York, 1963.

93. Dethier, V. G., and L. E. Chadwick. Chemoreception in insects. *Physiol. Revs.,* **28,** 220 (1948).

94. Devakul, V., and H. Maarse. A second compound in the odorous gland liquid of the giant water bug *Lethocerus indicus* (Lep. and Serv.). *Anal. Biochem.,* **7,** 269 (1964).

95. Dickins, G. R. The scent glands of certain Phycitidae (Lepidoptera). *Trans. Roy. Entomol. Soc. London,* **85,** 331 (1936).

95a. Doane, J. Movement on the soil surface, of adult *Ctenicera aeripennis destructor* (Brown) and *Hypolithus bicolor* Esch. (Coleoptera: Elateridae), as indicated by funnel pitfall traps, with notes on captures of other arthropods. *Can. Entomologist,* 93, 636 (1961).

96. Duane, J. P., and J. E. Tyler. Operation Saturnid. *Interchem. Rev.,* **9,** 25 (1950).

97. Dufay, C. Sur l'attraction sexuelle chez *Lasiocampa quercus* L. *Bull. soc. entomol. France,* **62,** 61 (1957).

98. Duges, as cited by Rau and Rau, reference 204.

98a. Dustan, G. G. Mating behaviour of the Oriental fruit moth, *Grapholitha molesta* (Busck) (Lepidoptera: Olethreutidae). *Can. Entomologist,* **96,** 1087 (1964).

99. Dyk, A. (1933), as cited by Farsky, reference 119.

100. Dyson, G. M. Some aspects of the vibration theory of odour. *Perfumery Essent. Oil Record,* **19,** 456 (1928).

101. Dyson, G. M. Raman effect and the concept of odour. *Perfumery Essent. Oil Record,* **28,** 13 (1937).

102. Dyson, G. M. The scientific basis of odour. *Chem. Ind. (London),* **16,** 647 (1938).

103. Dyson, G. M. Odour and chemical constitution. *Nature,* **173,** 831 (1954).

104. Eckstein, K. Auf neuen Wegen der Schädlingsbekämpfung. *Forstl. Wochschr. Silva,* **25,** 245 (1937).

105. Edelsten, H. M., and J. C. F. Fryer. Non-specific assembling scents in macro-lepidoptera. *Entomol. Record,* **56,** 7 (1944).

106. Eidmann, H. Morphologische und physiologische Untersuchungen am weiblichen Genitalapparat der Lepidopteren, I: Morphologischer Teil. *Z. angew. Entomol.,* **15,** 1 (1929).

107. Eidmann, H. Morphologische und physiologische Untersuchungen am weiblichen Genitalapparat der Lepidopteren, II: Physiologischer Teil. *Z. angew. Entomol.,* **18,** 57 (1931).

108. Eisner, T., and F. C. Kafatos. Defense mechanisms of arthropods, X: A pheromone promoting aggregation in an aposematic distasteful insect. *Psyche,* **69,** 53 (1962).

109. Eltringham, H. On the abdominal brushes in certain male noctuid moths. *Trans. Entomol. Soc. London,* **1925,** 1.

110. Emerson, A. E. The mechanism of tandem behavior following the colonizing flight in termites. *Anat. Record,* **57** (Suppl.), 61 (1933).
111. Engelmann, F. Hormonal control of mating behavior in an insect. *Experientia,* **16,** 69 (1960).
112. Evans, R. M. Hormones and related substances. The sex attractants of the gypsy moth. *Mfg. Chemist,* **32,** 175 (1961).
113. Evans, R. M. Hormones and related substances. Insect attractants. *Mfg. Chemist,* **33,** 472 (1962).
114. Evers, A. Über die Funktion der Excitatoren beim Liebesspiel der Malachiidae. *Entomol. Bl. (Krefeld),* **52,** 165 (1956).
115. Fabre, J. H. *Souvenirs Entomologiques,* 8th Ed., Paris, 1904.
116. Fabre, J. H. Hochzeitsflüge der Nachtpfauenaugen. *Kosmos,* **3,** 45 (1906).
117. Fabre, J. H. *The Life of the Caterpillar,* Dodd, Mead and Co., New York, 1916.
118. Farbenfabriken Bayer A. G. 10,12-Hexadecadiene derivatives. *Brit. Patent* 945.298 (Dec. 23, 1963).
119. Farsky, O. Nonnenkontroll- und Vorbeugungsmethode nach Professor Forst.- Ing. Ant. Dyk. *Anz. Schädlingskunde,* **14,** 52, 65 (1938).
120. Fattig, P. W. The Mutillidae or velvet ants of Georgia. *Emory Univ. Mus. Bull.,* no. **1,** 1 (1943).
121. Federley, H. Die Bedeutung der Kreuzung für die Evolution. *Jena. Z. Naturwissenschaft,* **67,** 364 (1932).
121a. Féron, M. Attraction chimique du mâle de *Ceratitis capitata* Wied. (Dipt. Trypetidae) pour la femelle. *Compt. rend.,* **248,** 2403 (1959).
121b. Féron, M. L'Instinct de reproduction chez la mouche Méditerranéenne des fruits *Ceratitis capitata* Wied. (Dipt. Trypetidae); comportement sexuel-comportement de ponte. *Rev. pathol. végétale et entomol. agr. France,* **41,** 1 (1962).
122. Fink, D. E. The biology of *Macrocentrus ancylivora* Rohwer, an important parasite of the strawberry leaf roller (*Ancylis comptana* Froehl). *J. Agr. Research,* **32,** 1121 (1926).
123. Flaschenträger, B. Über Anlockungsstoffe von Baumwollschädlingen. *Angew. Chem.,* **61,** 252 (1949).
124. Flaschenträger, B., and E. S. Amin. Chemical attractants for insects: sex- and food-odours of the cotton leaf worm and the cut worm. *Nature,* **165,** 394 (1950).
125. Flaschenträger, B., E. S. Amin, and H. J. Jarczyk. Ein Lockstoffanalysator (Odouranalyser) für Insekten. *Mikrochim. Acta,* **1957,** 385.
126. Forbush, E. H., and C. H. Fernald. *The Gypsy Moth,* Mass. State Board Agr., Boston, 1896.
127. Ford, E. B. Zygaenidae attracted by the female of *Lasiocampa quercus,* L. *Proc. Entomol. Soc. London,* **1,** 20 (1926).
128. Ford, E. B. *Moths,* Collins, London, 1955.

130   *Insect Sex Attractants*

129. Forel, A. *The Senses of Insects*, Methuen, London, 1908.
129a. Francke-Grosmann, H. Some new aspects in forest entomology. *Ann. Rev. Entomol.*, **8**, 415 (1963).
130. Franz, J. Die Tannentriebwickler *Cacoecia murinana* Hb. Beiträge zur Bionomie und Oekologie. *Z. angew. Entomol.*, **27**, 345 (1940).
131. Freiling, H. H. Duftorgane der weiblichen Schmetterlinge nebst Beiträgen zur Kenntnis der Sinnesorgane auf dem Schmetterlingsflügel und der Duftpinsel der Männchen von *Danais* und *Euploea*. *Z. wiss. Zool.*, **92**, 210 (1909).
132. Gade, G. Observations on the habits of *Pimpla* (*Rhyssa*) *lunator*. *Bull. Brooklyn Entomol. Soc.*, **7**, 103 (1884).
133. Gara, R. I. Studies on the flight behavior of *Ips confusus* (Lec.) (Coleoptera: Scolytidae) in response to attractive material. *Contrib. Boyce Thompson Inst.*, **22**, 51 (1963).
134. Gary, N. E. Queen honey bee attractiveness as related to mandibular gland secretion. *Science*, **133**, 1479 (1961).
135. Gary, N. E. Chemical mating attractants in the queen honey bee. *Science*, **135**, 773 (1962).
135a. Gaston, L. K., and H. H. Shorey. Sex pheromones of noctuid moths, IV: An apparatus for bioassaying the pheromones of six species. *Ann. Entomol. Soc. Am.*, **57**, 779 (1964).
135b. Gentry, C. R., F. R. Lawson, and J. D. Hoffman. A sex attractant in the tobacco budworm. *J. Econ. Entomol.*, **57**, 819 (1964).
136. Germer, F. Untersuchungen über den Bau und die Lebensweise der Lymexyloniden, speziell des *Hylecoetus dermestoides* L. *Z. wiss. Zool.*, **101**, 683 (1912).
136a. Girault, A. A. The lesser peach tree borer. *U. S. Dept. Agr. Bur. Entomol. Bull.*, No. 68, (Pt. IV), 31 (1907).
137. Görnitz, K. Anlockversuche mit dem weiblichen Sexualduftstoff des Schwammspinners (*Lymantria dispar*) und der Nonne (*Lymantria monacha*). *Anz. Schädlingskunde*, **22**, 145 (1949).
138. Götz, B. Untersuchungen über die Wirkung des Sexualduftstoffes bei den Traubenwicklern *Clysia ambiguella* und *Polychrosis botrana*. *Z. angew. Entomol.*, **26**, 143 (1939).
139. Götz, B. Über weitere Versuche zur Bekämpfung der Traubenwickler mit Hilfe des Sexualduftstoffes. *Anz. Schädlingskunde*, **15**, 109 (1939).
140. Götz, B. Sexualduftstoffe als Lockmittel in der Schädlingsbekämpfung. *Umschau*, **44**, 794 (1940).
141. Götz, B. Lockflüssigkeiten zur Beobachtung des Traubenwicklermottenfluges. *Wein Rebe*, **22**, 15 (1940).
142. Götz, B. Neue Apparate zum Studium der Insektenphysiologie. *Umschau*, **45**, 779 (1941).
143. Götz, B. Der Sexualduftstoff als Bekämpfungsmittel gegen die Traubenwickler im Freiland. *Wein Rebe*, **23**, 75 (1941).

144. Götz, B. Beiträge zur Analyse des Mottenfluges bei den Trauben-wicklern *Clysia ambiguella* und *Polychrosis botrana. Wein Rebe,* **23,** 207 (1941).

145. Götz, B. Die Sexualduftstoffe an Lepidopteren. *Experientia,* 7, 406 (1951).

146. Graham, H. M., and D. F. Martin. Use of cyanide in pink boll-worm sex-lure traps. *J. Econ. Entomol.,* **56,** 901 (1963).

147. Green, E. E. Notes on assembling of males of certain moths in Ceylon. *Entomol. Monthly Mag.,* **35,** 258 (1899).

147a. Green, N., M. Beroza, and S. A. Hall. Recent developments in chemical attractants for insects. *Adv. Pest Control Research,* **3,** 129 (1960).

148. Grosch, D. S. The importance of antennae in the mating reaction of male *Habrobracon. J. Comp. Physiol. Psychol.,* **40,** 23 (1947).

149. Grosch, D. S. Experimental studies on the mating reaction of male *Habrobracon. J. Comp. Physiol. Psychol.,* **41,** 188 (1948).

150. Guex, W., R. Rüegg, and U. Schwieter. Verfahren zur Herstellung von ungesättigten, gegebenenfalls veresterten Alkoholen. Ger. Patent 1,111,615 (July 27, 1961).

151. Gupta, A. P. A critical review of the studies on the so-called stink or repugnatorial glands of Heteroptera with further comments. *Can. Entomologist,* **93,** 482 (1961).

152. Gupta, A. P. Musculature and mechanism of the nymphal scent-apparatus of *Riptortus linearis* H. S. (Heteroptera: Alydidae) with comments on the number, variation and homology of the abdominal scent glands in other Heteroptera. *Proc. Entomol. Soc. Wash., D. C.,* **66,** 12 (1964).

153. Haase, E. Dufteinrichtungen indischer Schmetterlinge. *Zool. Anz.,* **11,** 475 (1888).

154. Haller, H. L., F. Acree. Jr., and S. F. Potts. The nature of the sex attractant of the female gypsy moth. *J. Am. Chem. Soc.,* **66,** 1659 (1944).

155. Hamm, A. H. Persistent odour of *Bombyx quercus. Entomol. Monthly Mag.,* **6,** 74 (1895).

156. Hammad, S. M., and H. J. Jarczyk. Contributions to the biology and biochemistry of the cotton leaf-worm, *Prodenia litura* F., III: The morphology and histology of the sexual scent glands of the female moth of *Prodenia litura* F. *Bull. soc. roy. entomol. Egypt,* **51,** 253 (1958).

157. Hanno, K. Anlockversuche bei *Lymantria monacha* L. *Z. angew. Entomol.,* **25,** 628 (1939).

158. Hardy, E. Scents from insects. Butterfly and moth perfumes and their extraction. *Perfumery Essent. Oil Record,* **38,** 403 (1947).

159. Hardy, E. Do insects locate each other by scent or wireless? *Beama J.,* **56,** 257 (1949).

160. Hatanaka, A. Chemie über den Sexuallockstoff der Insekten. *Botyu-Kagaku*, **28**, 110 (1963).

161. Hauser, G. Physiologische und histologische Untersuchungen über das Geruchsorgan der Insekten. *Z. wiss. Zool.*, **34**, 367 (1880).

162. Hecker, E. Isolation and characterization of the sex attractant of the silk worm moth (*Bombyx mori* L.). *Proc. Xth Intern. Cong. Entomol.*, **2**, 293 (1956) (Pub. 1958).

163. Hecker, E. Sexuallockstoffe—hochwirksame Parfüms der Schmetterlinge, I: *Umschau*, **63**, 465 (1959).

164. Hecker, E. Sexuallockstoffe—hochwirksame Parfüms der Schmetterlinge, II: *Umschau*, **63**, 499 (1959).

165. Hecker, E. Chemie und Biochemie des Sexuallockstoffes des Seidenspinners (*Bombyx mori*). *Proc. XIth Intern. Cong. Entomol.*, **3B**, 69 (1960) (Pub. 1961).

165a. Henneberry, T. J., and A. F. Howland. *J. Econ. Entomol.*, in press.

166. Henneberry, T. J., and W. L. McGovern. Effect of gamma radiation on mating competitiveness and behavior of *Drosophila melanogaster* males. *J. Econ. Entomol.*, **56**, 739 (1963).

167. Hering, M. (1926). *Biologie der Schmetterlinge*, Julius Springer Verlag, Berlin, pp. 145–159.

168. Hesse, R., and F. Doflein. (1910), *Tierbau und Tierleben*, Vol. 1, B. G. Teubner Verlag, Leipzig, pp. 644–645.

169. Hesse, R., and F. Doflein. (1910), *Tierbau und Tierleben*, Vol. 2, B. G. Teubner Verlag, Leipzig, pp. 437–438.

170. Hillaby, J. Smell chemistry of moths studied. *The New York Times*, May 19, 1963.

170a. Hoffman, J. D. The influence of virgin females on catches of black light traps. *Bull. Entomol. Soc. Am.*, **10**, 170 (1964).

171. Holbrook, R. F., M. Beroza, and E. D. Burgess. Gypsy moth (*Porthetria dispar*) detection with the natural female sex lure. *J. Econ. Entomol.*, **53**, 751 (1960).

172. Hurd, P. D. The California velvet ants of the genus *Dasymutilla* Ashmead (Hymenoptera: Mutillidae). *Bull. Calif. Insect Survey*, **1**, 89 (1951).

173. Ignoffo, C. M., R. S. Berger, H. M. Graham, and D. F. Martin. Sex attractant of *Trichoplusia ni* (Hübner) (Lepidoptera:Noctuidae). *Science*, **141**, 902 (1963).

174. Illig, K. G. Duftorgane der männlichen Schmetterlinge. *Zoologica* (*Stuttgart*), **15** (38), 34 pp. (1902).

175. Inhoffen, H. H. Versuch zur Isolierung eines Sexual-Lockstoffes. *Arch. Pharm.*, **284**, 337 (1951).

176. Inoue, Y., and M. Ohno. Insect attractants. *Kagaku no Ryoiki*, **15**, 823 (1961).

177. Jacentkovski (1932), as cited by Farsky, reference 119.

178. Jacentkovski (1934), as cited by Farsky, reference 119.

179. Jacobson, M. Attractants for the gypsy moth. U. S. Patent 2,900,756 (Aug. 25, 1959).
180. Jacobson, M. Synthesis of a highly potent gypsy moth sex attractant. *J. Org. Chem.*, **25**, 2074 (1960).
181. Jacobson, M. Method of attracting male gypsy moth with 12-acetoxy-1-hydroxy-9-octadecene. U. S. Patent 3,018,219 (Jan. 23, 1962).
182. Jacobson, M. 12-Acetoxy-1-hydroxy-9-octadecene and method for producing the same. U. S. Patent 3,050,551 (Aug. 21, 1962).
183. Jacobson, M. Insect sex attractants, III: The optical resolution of *dl*-10-acetoxy-*cis*-7-hexadecen-1-ol. *J. Org. Chem.*, **27**, 2670 (1962).
184. Jacobson, M. Recent progress in the chemistry of insect sex attractants. *Advances in Chem. Ser.*, no. **41**, 1 (1963).
184a. Jacobson, M. The sensitivity of insects to sexual olfactory stimuli. *Am. Heart J.*, **68**, 577 (1964).
185. Jacobson, M., and M. Beroza. Chemical insect attractants. *Science*, **140**, 1367 (1963).
186. Jacobson, M., and M. Beroza. Sex attractant of the American cockroach. *Science*, **142**, 1258 (1963).
187. Jacobson, M., and M. Beroza. Insect attractants. *Sci. American*, **211** (2), 20 (1964).
187a. Jacobson, M., and M. Beroza. American cockroach sex attractant. *Science*, **147**, 748 (1965).
188. Jacobson, M., M. Beroza, and W. A. Jones. Isolation, identification, and synthesis of the sex attractant of gypsy moth. *Science*, **132**, 1011 (1960).
189. Jacobson, M., M. Beroza, and W. A. Jones. Insect sex attractants, I: The isolation, identification and synthesis of the sex attractant of the gypsy moth. *J. Am. Chem. Soc.*, **83**, 4819 (1961).
190. Jacobson, M., M. Beroza, and R. T. Yamamoto. Isolation and identification of the sex attractant of the American cockroach. *Science*, **139**, 48 (1963).
191. Jacobson, M., and W. A. Jones. Insect sex attractants, II: The synthesis of a highly potent gypsy moth sex attractant and some related compounds. *J. Org. Chem.*, **27**, 2523 (1962).
191a. Jeannel, R. *Introduction to Entomology*, Hutchinson, London, 1960.
192. Jones, W. A., and M. Jacobson. Insect sex attractants, IV: The determination of gyplure in its mixtures by adsorption and gas chromatography. *J. Chromatog.*, **14**, 22 (1964).
193. Jones, W. A., and M. Jacobson. Insect sex attractants, V: The synthesis of some additional compounds related to gyplure. *J. Med. Chem.*, **7**, 373 (1964).
194. Karlson, P. Pheromones. *Ergeb. Biol.*, **22**, 212 (1960).
195. Karlson, P., and A. Butenandt. Pheromones (ectohormones) in insects. *Ann. Rev. Entomol.*, **4**, 39 (1959).

196. Karlson, P., and M. Lüscher. "Pheromone," ein Nomenklatur-vorschlag für eine Wirkstoffklasse. *Naturwissenschaften*, **46**, 63 (1959).

197. Karlson, P., and M. Lüscher. "Pheromones": a new term for a class of biologically active substances. *Nature*, **183**, 1835 (1959).

198. Keller, J. C., E. B. Mitchell, G. McKibben, and T. B. Davich. A sex attractant for female boll weevils from males. *J. Econ. Entomol.*, **57**, 609 (1964).

199. Kellogg, V. L. Some silkworm moth reflexes. *Biol. Bull. Marine Biol. Lab.*, **12**, 152 (1907).

199a. Kelner-Pillault, S. Attirence sexuelle chez *Mantis religiosa* (Orth.). *Bull. soc. entomol. France*, **62**, 9 (1957).

200. Kettlewell, H. B. D. The assembling scent of *Arctia villica* and *Parasemia plantaginis*. *Entomol. Record*, **54**, 62 (1942).

201. Kettlewell, H. B. D. Further observations on non-specific assembling scents in macro-Lepidoptera. *Entomol. Record*, **55**, 107 (1943).

202. Kettlewell, H. B. D. Female assembling scents with reference to an important paper on the subject. *Entomologist*, **79**, 8 (1946).

203. Kettlewell, H. B. D. The radiation theory of female assembling in the Lepidoptera. *Entomologist*, **94**, 59 (1961).

204. King, H. Sex attractant principles of moths. *Proc. South London Entomol. Nat. Hist. Soc.*, **1946–47**, 106 (1947).

205. Kirkland, A. H. (1893), as cited by Farsky, reference 119.

206. Kirkland, A. H. (1896), as cited by Forbush and Fernald, reference 126.

207. Kirschenblatt, J. D. Klassifikation einiger biologisch aktiven Stoffe, die von den tierischen Organismen ausgearbeitet werden. *Trav. soc. naturalistes Leningrad*, **73** (4), 225 (1957).

208. Kirschenblatt, J. D. Telergones and their biological significance. *Uspekhi Sovremenroi Biol.*, **46**, 322 (1958).

209. Kirschenblatt, J. D. Terminology of some biologically active substances and validity of the term "pheromones." *Nature*, **195**, 916 (1962).

210. Kliefoth, R. A., J. P. Vité, and G. B. Pitman. A laboratory technique for testing bark beetle attractants. *Contrib. Boyce Thompson Inst.*, **22**, 283 (1964).

211. Kliewer, J. W., and T. Miura. Sex attractants of mosquitoes. *Abstr. Pacific Branch Meeting, Entomol. Soc. Am.*, **1964**, 11.

212. Koch, W., *Synthesis of Bombykol, the Sex Attractant of the Silkworm Moth, and its Geometric Isomers*, Doctoral Dissertation, Fac. Sci. Univ. Munich, Ger. (July 30, 1962).

213. Komarek, I., and A. Pfeffer. Eine neue biologische Kontrolle der Forstschädlinge. *Verhandl. VIIth Intern. Cong. Entomol.*, **3**, 200 (1938) (Pub. 1939).

214. Kullenberg, B. Some observations on scents among bees and wasps (Hymenoptera). *Entomol. Tidskr.*, **74**, 1 (1953).

215. Kullenberg, B. Field experiments with chemical sexual attractants on aculeate Hymenoptera males. *Zool. Bidrag. fran Uppsala*, **31**, 253 (1956).

216. Kullenberg, B. Studies in *Ophrys* pollination. *Zool. Bidrag. fran Uppsala*, **34**, 1 (1961).

217. Kunike, G. Zur Biologie der kleinen Wachsmotte, *Achroea grisella* Fabr. *Z. angew. Entomol.*, **16**, 304 (1930).

218. Laithwaite, E. R. A radiation theory of the asembling of moths. *Entomologist*, **93**, 113, 133 (1960).

219. Lane, M. C. Recent progress in the control of wireworms. *World's Grain Exhibition Conf., Regina, Can.*, **2**, 529 (1933).

220. Lederer, E. Odeurs et parfums des animaux. *Fortschr. Chem. org. Naturstoffe*, **6**, 87 (1950).

221. Lefebvre, A. Note sur le sentiment olfactif des antennes. *Ann. soc. entomol. France*, [1], **7**, 395 (1838).

222. Lehman, R. S. Experiments to determine the attractiveness of various aromatic compounds to adults of the wireworm, *Limonius (Pheletes) canus* Lec. and *Limonius (Pheletes) californicus* Mann. *J. Econ. Entomol.*, **25**, 949 (1932).

223. Lehmensick, R., and R. Liebers. Beiträge zur Biologie der Micro-lepidopteren. (Untersuchungen an *Plodia interpunctella* Hb.). *Z. angew. Entomol.*, **24**, 582 (1938).

224. Lemarie, J. Neue Kontrollmethode des Nonnenvorkommens. *Anz. Schädlingskunde*, **9**, 43 (1933).

224a. Lhoste, J., and A. Roche. Organes odoriférants des mâles de *Ceratitis capitata*. *Bull. soc. entomol. France*, **65**, 206 (1960).

225. Lilly, C. E. Response of males of *Limonius californicus* (Mann.) (Coleoptera: Elateridae) to a sex attractant separable by paper chromatography. *Can. Entomologist*, **91**, 145 (1959).

225a. Lilly, C. E., and A. J. McGinnis. Reactions of male click beetles in the laboratory to olfactory pheromones. *Can. Entomologist*, **97**, 317 (1965).

226. Magnus, D. Beobachtungen zur Balz und Eiablage des Kaisermantels *Argynnis paphia* L. (Lep., Nymphalidae). *Z. Tierpsychol.*, **7**, 435 (1950).

227. Makino, K., K. Satoh, and K. Inagami. Bombixin, a sex attractant discharged by female moth, *Bombyx mori. Biochem. Biophys. Acta*, **19**, 394 (1956).

228. Maksimović, M. Testing of trap method for capturing the gypsy moth males. *Zashtita Bilja (Pest Control)*, no. **52–53**, 177 (1959).

229. Maksimović, M. Sex attractant traps with female odour of the gypsy moth used for forecasting the increase of population of gypsy moth. *Programme XIIth Intern. Cong. Entomol., London*, **1964**, 69.

230. Marshall, J. The location of olfactory receptors in insects: a review of experimental evidence. *Trans. Roy. Entomol. Soc. London*, **83**, 49 (1935).

231. Matthes, D. Excitatoren und Paarungsverhalten mitteleuropäischer Malachiiden (Coleopt., Malacodermata). *Z. Morphol. Ökol. Tiere*, **51**, 375 (1962).

232. Mayer, A. G. On the mating instinct in moths. *Psyche*, **9**, 15 (1900).

233. Mayer, A. G., and C. G. Soule. Some reactions of caterpillars and moths. *J. Exptl. Zool.*, **3**, 415 (1906).

233a. Mayr, E. The role of the antennae in the mating behavior of female *Drosophila*. *Evolution*, **4**, 149 (1950).

234. McIndoo, N. E. The olfactory sense of Coleoptera. *Biol. Bull.*, **28**, 407 (1915).

235. Mell, R., *Biologie und Systematik der südchinesischen Sphingiden*, Friedländer, Berlin, 1922.

236. Micklem, H. S. The proposed biological term "pheromone." *Nature*, **183**, 1835 (1959).

237. Minnich, D. E. The chemical senses of insects. *Quart. Rev. Biol.*, **4**, 100 (1929).

238. Moncrieff, R. W. *The Chemical Senses*, Leonard Hill, London, 1944.

239. Moncrieff, R. W. The gypsy moth may provide the perfumer with a new fixative. *Mfg. Chemist Mfg. Perfumer*, **16**, 167 (1945).

240. Morita, H., and S. Yamashita. Receptor potentials recorded from sensilla basiconica on the antenna of the silkworm larvae, *Bombyx mori*. *J. Exptl. Biol.*, **38**, 851 (1961).

241. Morse, R. A. Swarm orientation in honeybees. *Science*, **141**, 357 (1963).

242. Morse, R. A., N. E. Gary, and T. S. K. Johansson. Mating of virgin queen honey bees (*Apis mellifera* L.) following mandibular gland extirpation. *Nature*, **194**, 605 (1962).

243. Müller, F. Notes on Brazilian entomology. *Trans. Entomol. Soc. London*, **1878**, 211.

244. Müller, F., as cited by Rau and Rau, reference 268.

245. Müller, K. Histologische Untersuchungen über den Entwicklungsbeginn bei einem Kleinschmetterling (*Plodia interpunctella*). *Z. wiss. Zool.*, **151**, 192 (1938).

246. Murr, L. Über den Geruchsinn der Mehlmottenschlupfwespe *Habrobracon juglandis* Ashmead. *Z. vergl. Physiol.*, **11**, 210 (1930).

247. Nakazema, S. Notes on the response of the silkworm (*Bombyx mori* L.) to odors, III: On the olfactory sense of the adult moth. *Bull. Miyazaki Coll. Agr. Forestry*, no. 3, 129 (1931).

248. Nichols, J. O. The gypsy moth in Pennsylvania—its history and eradication. *Penna. Dept. Agr. Misc. Bull.*, no. **4404**, 82 pp. (1961).

249. Nolte, H. W. Neue Erfahrungen zur Dykschen Nonnenanlockmethode. *Centrbl. ges. Forstw.*, **66**, 197, 252 (1940).

250. Norris, M. J. Contributions towards the study of insect fertility, II: Experiments on the factors influencing fertility in *Ephestia*

kühniella Z. (Lepidoptera, Phycitidae). *Proc. Zool. Soc. London,* **1933**, 903.

251. Ouye, M. T., and B. A. Butt. A natural sex lure extracted from female pink bollworms. *J. Econ. Entomol.,* **55,** 419 (1962).

252. Ouye, M. T., H. M. Graham, C. A. Richmond, and D. F. Martin. Mating studies of the pink bollworm. *J. Econ. Entomol.,* **57,** 222 (1964).

253. Pain, J., M. Barbier, D. Bogdanovsky, and E. Lederer. Chemistry and biological activity of the secretions of queen and worker honeybees (*Apis mellifica* L.). *Comp. Biochem. Physiol.,* **6,** 233 (1962).

254. Pain, J., and F. Ruttner. Les extraits des glandes mandibulaires des reines d'abeilles attirent les mâles, lors du vol nuptial. *Compt. rend.,* **256,** 512 (1963).

255. Park, R. J., and M D. Sutherland. Volatile constituents of the bronze orange bug, *Rhoecocoris sulciventris. Austral. J. Chem.,* **15,** 172 (1962).

256. Parker, H. L. *Macrocentrus gifuensis* Ashmead, a polyembryonic braconid parasite in the European corn borer. *U. S. Dept. Agr. Tech. Bull.,* no. **230,** 62 pp. (1931).

257. Parkes, A. S. Olfactory effects in mammalian reproduction. *Endocrinol. Japon.,* **9,** 247 (1962).

257a. Perez, R., and W. H. Long. Sex attractant and mating behavior in the sugarcane borer. *J. Econ. Entomol.,* **57,** 688 (1964).

258. Petersen, W. Die Morphologie der Generationsorgane der Schmetterlinge und ihre Bedeutung für die Artbildung. *Mem. Acad. Imp. Sci. St. Petersburg,* [8], **16** (8), 84 pp. (1904).

259. Pitman, G. B., and J. P. Vité. Studies on the pheromone of *Ips confusus* (Lec.), I: Secondary sexual dimorphism in the hindgut epithelium. *Contrib. Boyce Thompson Inst.,* **22,** 221 (1963).

260. Pointing, P. J. The biology and behavior of the European pine shoot moth, *Rhyacionia buoliana* (Schiff.) in Southern Ontario, I: Adult. *Can. Entomologist,* **93,** 1098 (1961).

261. Prüffer, J. Observations et expériences sur les phénomènes de la vie sexuelle de *Lymantria dispar* L. *Bull. Intern. Acad. Polon. Sci. Lettres,* [B], No. **1,** 1 (1923) (Pub. 1924).

262. Prüffer, J. Untersuchungen über die Innervierung der Fühler bei *Saturnia pyri* L. *Zool. Jahrb., Abt. Anat. Ontog. Tiere,* **51,** 1 (1929).

263. Prüffer, J. Weitere Untersuchungen über die Männchenanlockung bei *Lymantria dispar* L. (Lep.). *Zool. Polon.,* **2,** 43 (1937).

264. Puls, W., G. L. Haberland, and K. Schlossmann. Über Wirkungen des Hexadecadien-(10,12)-ol-(1) auf den Stoffwechsel der Ratte. *Naturwissenschaften,* **50,** 671 (1963).

264a. Putman, W. L. The codling moth, *Carpocapsa pomonella* (L.)

(Lepidoptera: Tortricidae): a review with special reference to Ontario. *Proc. Entomol. Soc. Ontario*, **93**, 22 (1962) (Pub. 1963).

264b. Rathmayer, W. Sexuallockstoffe bei Hymenopteren. *Naturw. Rundschau*, **14**, 153 (1961).

265. Rau, P. Sexual selection experiments in the cecropia moth. *Trans. Acad Sci. St. Louis*, **20**, 275 (1911).

266. Rau, P. Further observations on copulation and oviposition in *Samia cecropia* Linn. *Trans. Acad. Sci. St. Louis*, **20**, 309 (1911).

267. Rau, P. A note on the courtship of *Telea polyphemus. Can. Entomologist*, **56**, 271 (1924).

268. Rau, P., and N. L. Rau. The sex attraction and rhythmic periodicity in the giant saturniid moths. *Trans. Acad. Sci. St. Louis*, **26**, 83 (1929).

269. Reichenau (1880), as cited by Dickins, reference 95.

270. Renner, M. Das Duftorgan der Honigbiene und die physiologische Bedeutung ihres Lockduftes. *Z. vergl. Physiol.*, **43**, 411 (1960).

271. Ribbands, C. R., *The Behavior and Social Life of Honeybees*, Bee Research Assoc., Ltd., London, 1953.

272. Richards, O. W., Sexual selection and allied problems in the insects. *Biol. Revs.*, **2**, 298 (1927).

273. Richards, O. W., and W. S. Thomson. A contribution to the study of the genera *Ephestia*, GN. (including *Strymax*, Dyar), and *Plodia*, GN. (Lepidoptera, Phycitidae), with notes on parasites of the larvae. *Trans. Entomol. Soc. London*, **80**, 169 (1932).

274. Riemschneider, R., and G. Kasang. Stereoisomere des Heptade-cadien-(10.12)-ols-(1). *Z. Naturforsch.*, **18b**, 646 (1963).

275. Riley, C. V. The senses of insects. *Insect Life*, **7**, 33 (1894).

276. Riley, C. V. The senses of insects. *Insect Life*, **7**, 38 (1894).

276a. Roever, K. Bionomics of *Agathymus* (Megathymidae). *J. Research Lepidoptera*, **3**, 103 (1964).

277. Rogoff, W. M. Biological aspects of the house fly sex pheromone. *Abstr. Pacific Branch Meeting, Entomol. Soc. Am.*, **1964**, 7.

278. Rogoff, W. M., A. D. Beltz, J. O. Johnsen, and F. W. Plapp. A sex pheromone in the housefly, *Musca domestica* L. *J. Insect Physiol.*, **10**, 239 (1964).

279. Röller, H., H. Piepho, and I. Holz. Zum Problem der Hormonab-hängigkeit des Paarungsverhaltens bei Insekten. Untersuchungen an *Galleria mellonella* (L.). *J. Insect Physiol.*, **9**, 187 (1963).

280. Roth, L. M. Hypersexual activity induced in females of the cock-roach *Nauphoeta cinerea. Science*, **138**, 1267 (1962).

280a. Roth, L. M., and R. H. Barth, Jr. The control of sexual receptivity in female cockroaches. *J. Insect Physiol.*, **10**, 965 (1964).

281. Roth, L. M., and E. R. Willis. A study of cockroach behavior. *Am. Midland Naturalist*, **47**, 66 (1952).

282. Roth, L. M., and E. R. Willis. Observations on the behavior of the webbing clothes moth. *J. Econ. Entomol.*, **45**, 20 (1952).

282a. Roth, L. M., and E. R. Willis. The reproduction of cockroaches. *Smithsonian Inst. Publs. Misc. Collections*, **122**, 1 (1954).

283. Roth, L. M., and E. R. Willis. Intra-uterine nutrition of the "beetle-roach" *Diploptera dytiscoides* (Serv.) during embryogenesis, with notes on its biology in the laboratory (Blattaria: Diplopteridae). *Psyche*, **62**, 55 (1955).

284. Rudinsky, J. A. Response of *Dendroctonus pseudotsugae* Hopkins to volatile attractants. *Contrib. Boyce Thompson Inst.*, **22**, 23 (1963).

284a. Rudinsky, J. A., and G. E. Daterman. Response of the ambrosia beetle *Trypodendron lineatum* (Oliv.) to a female-produced phero-mone. *Z. angew. Entomol.*, **54**, 300 (1964).

284b. Rudinsky, J. A., and G. E. Daterman. Field studies on flight patterns and olfactory responses of ambrosia beetles in Douglas-fir forests of western Oregon. *Can. Entomologist*, **96**, 1339 (1964).

285. Ruttner, F. Die Sexualfunktionen der Honigbienen im Dienste ihrer sozialen Gemeinschaft. *Z. vergl. Physiol.*, **39**, 577 (1957).

286. Saunders, H. C. The stereochemical theory of olfaction, 5: Some odor observations in terms of the Amoore theory. *Proc. Toilet Goods Assoc.*, *Sci. Sect.*, no. **37** (Suppl.), 46 (1962).

287. Schedl, K. E. Der Schwammspinner (*Porthetria dispar* L.) in Euroasien, Afrika und Neuengland. *Monograph. angew. Entomol.*, no. **12**, 242 pp. (1936).

288. Schenk, O. Die antennale Hautsinnesorgane einiger Lepidopteren und Hymenopteren mit besonderer Berücksichtigung der sexuellen Unterschiede. *Zool. Jahrb.*, *Abt. Anat. Ontog. Tiere*, **17**, 573 (1903).

289. Schlinger, E. I., and J. C. Hall. The biology, behavior and morphology of *Praon pallitans* Muesebeck, an internal parasite of the spotted alfalfa aphid, *Therioaphis maculata* (Buckton) (Hymenoptera: Braconidae, Aphidiinae). *Ann. Entomol. Soc. Am.*, **53**, 144 (1960).

290. Schneider, D. Elektrophysiologische Untersuchungen von Chemo- und Mechanorezeptoren der Antenne des Seidenspinners *Bombyx mori* L. *Z. vergl. Physiol.*, **40**, 8 (1957).

291. Schneider, D. Untersuchungen zum Bau und zur Funktion der Riechorgane von Schmetterlingen und Käfern. *Ber. Phys.-Med. Ges. Würzburg*, [N.S.], **70**, 158 (1960–1961) (Pub. 1961).

292. Schneider, D. Der Geruchssinn bei den Insekten. *Dragoco Ber.*, **2**, 27 (1961).

293. Schneider, D. Electrophysiological investigation on the olfactory specificity of sexual attracting substances in different species of moths. *J. Insect Physiol.*, **8**, 15 (1962).

294. Schneider, D. Electrophysiological investigation of insect olfaction. *Proc. First Intern. Symposium Olfaction Taste*, **1963**, 85.

294a. Schneider, D. Function of insect olfactory sensilla. *Proc. XVIth Intern. Cong. Zool.*, *Washington*, **3**, 84 (1963).

294b. Schneider, D. Vergleichende Rezeptorphysiologie am Beispiel der Riechorgane von Insekten. *Jahrb. Max-Planck-Ges. Förd. Wiss.*, **1963**, 150 (Pub. 1964).

295. Schneider, D. Insect antennae. *Ann. Rev. Entomol.*, **9**, 103 (1964).

296. Schneider, D., and E. Hecker. Zur Elektrophysiologie der Antenne des Seidenspinners *Bombyx mori* bei Reizung mit angereicherten Extrakten des Sexuallockstoffes. *Z. Naturforsch.*, **11b**, 121 (1956).

297. Schneider, D., and K. E. Kaissling. Der Bau der Antenne des Seidenspinners *Bombyx mori* L., I: Architektur und Bewegungsapparat der Antenne sowie Struktur der Cuticula. *Zool. Jahrb., Abt. Anat. Ontog. Tiere*, **75**, 287 (1956).

298. Schneider, D., and K. E. Kaissling. Der Bau der Antenne des Seidenspinners *Bombyx mori* L., II: Sensillen, cuticulare Bildung und innerer Bau. *Zool. Jahrb., Abt. Anat. Ontog. Tiere*, **76**, 223 (1957).

299. Schneider, D., and K. E. Kaissling. Der Bau der Antenne des Seidenspinners *Bombyx mori* L., III: Das Bindegewebe und das Blutgefäss. *Zool. Jahrb., Abt. Anat. Ontog. Tiere*, **77**, 111 (1959).

299a. Schneider, D., V. Lacher, and K. E. Kaissling. Die Reaktionsweise und das Reaktionsspektrum von Riechzellen bei *Antheraea pernyi* (Lepidoptera, Saturniidae). *Z. vergl. Physiol.*, **48**, 632 (1964).

300. Schwinck, I. Über den Sexualduftstoff der Pyraliden. *Z. vergl. Physiol.*, **35**, 167 (1953).

301. Schwinck, I. Experimentelle Untersuchungen über Geruchssinn und Strömungswahrnehmung in der Orientierung bei Nachtschmetterlingen. *Z. vergl. Physiol.*, **37**, 19 (1954).

302. Schwinck, I. Freilandversuche zur Frage der Artspezifität des weiblichen Sexualduftstoffes der Nonne (*Lymantria monacha* L.) und des Schwammspinners (*Lymantria dispar* L.). *Z. angew. Entomol.*, **37**, 349 (1955).

303. Schwinck, I. Weitere Untersuchungen zur Frage des Geruchsorientierung der Nachtschmetterlinge: Partielle Fühleramputation bei Spinnermännchen, insbesondere am Seidenspinner *Bombyx mori* L. *Z. vergl. Physiol.*, **37**, 439 (1955).

304. Schwinck, I. A study of olfactory stimuli in the orientation of moths. *Proc. Xth Intern. Cong. Entomol.*, **2**, 577 (1956) (Pub. 1958).

305. Seiler, J. Resultate aus der Artkreuzung zwischen *Solenobia triquetrella* F.R. und *Solenobia fumosella* H. mit. Intersexualität in F_1. *Arch. Julius Klaus Stiftg.*, **24**, 124 (1949).

306. Seiler, J., and O. Puchta. Die Fortpflanzungsbiologie der Solenobien (Lepid. Psychidae), Verhalten bei Artkreuzungen und F_1-Resultate. *Wilhelm Roux Arch. Entwicklungsmech. Organismen*, **149**, 115 (1956).

307. Seitz, A. (1894), as cited by Urbahn, reference 339.

307a. Sekul, A. A., and H. C. Cox. Mating stimulant in the fall armyworm, *Laphygma frugiperda* (J. E. Smith). *Bull. Entomol. Soc. Am.*, **10**, 167 (1964).

308. Sengün, A. Über die biologische Bedeutung des Duftstoffes von *Bombyx mori* L. *Rev. fac. sci. univ. Istanbul*, [B], **19**, 281 (1954).

309. Sharma, S. L., and M. Z. Hussein. A pest of wild Saccharums in Bihar: *Mahasena graminivorum* Hampson (family Psychidae: Lepidoptera). *Indian J. Entomol.*, **17**, 89 (1955).

310. Shirck, F. H. The flight of sugar-beet wireworm adults in southwestern Idaho. *J. Econ. Entomol.*, **35**, 423 (1942).

311. Shorey, H. H. Nature of the sound produced by *Drosophila melanogaster* during courtship. *Science*, **137**, 677 (1962).

312. Shorey, H. H. Sex pheromones of noctuid moths, II: Mating behavior of *Trichoplusia ni* (Lepidoptera: Noctuidae) with special reference to the role of the sex pheromone. *Ann. Entomol. Soc. Am.*, **57**, 371 (1964).

313. Shorey, H. H., L. A. Andres, and R. L. Hales, Jr. The biology of *Trichoplusia ni* (Lepidoptera: Noctuidae), I: Life history and behavior. *Ann. Entomol. Soc. Am.*, **55**, 591 (1962).

313a. Shorey, H. H., and L. K. Gaston. Sex pheromones of noctuid moths, III: Inhibition of male responses to the sex pheromone in *Trichoplusia ni* (Lepidoptera: Noctuidae). *Ann. Entomol. Soc. Am.*, **57**, 775 (1964).

313b. Shorey, H. H., and L. K. Gaston. *Ann. Entomol. Soc. Am.*, in press.

314. Shorey, H. H., L. K. Gaston, and T. R. Fukuto. Sex pheromones of noctuid moths, I: A quantitative bioassay for the sex pheromone of *Trichoplusia ni* (Lepidoptera: Noctuidae). *J. Econ. Entomol.*, **57**, 252 (1964).

314a. Siebold. C. T. v. Die Spermatozoën wirbellosen Tiere, IV: Die Spermatozoën in dem befruchteten Insektenweibchen. *Arch. Anat. Physiol.*, **1837**, 381.

315. Simpson, J. Queen perception by honey bee swarms. *Nature*, **190**, 94 (1963).

315a. Smith, E. H. Laboratory rearing of the peach tree borer and notes on its biology. *J. Econ. Entomol.*, **58**, 228 (1965).

315b. Smyth, T. Mating behavior of the Madeira cockroach. *Abstr. Eastern Branch Meeting Entomol. Soc. Am.*, (1963).

316. Soule, C. G. Notes on the mating of *Attacus cecropia* and others. *Psyche*, **9**, 224 (1901).

316a. Soo Hoo, C. F., and R. J. Roberts. Sex attraction in *Rhopaea* (Coleoptera: Scarabaeidae). *Nature*, **205**, 724 (1965).

317. Soule, C. G., and Elliott, as cited by Rau and Rau, reference 268.

318. Spieth, H. T. Mating behavior within the genus *Drosophila* (Diptera). *Bull. Am. Mus. Nat. Hist.*, **99**, 397 (1952).

319. Standfuss, M., *Handbuch der Paläarktischen Gross-Schmetterlinge für Forscher und Sammler*, 2nd Ed., Jena, 1896.

320. Stefanović, D. K., B. Grujić-Injac, and D. Micic. Effect of optical activity on the synthetic of the sexual odor of the gypsy moth

female (gyptol and the higher homolog of gyplure). *Zashtita Bilja* (*Pest Control*), no. **73**, 235 (1963).

321. Stefanović, G., and B. Grujić. Chemical investigation of the active substance from the female gypsy moth, II: *Zashtita Bilja* (*Pest Control*), no. **56**, 94 (1959).

322. Stefanović, G., B. Grujić, and P. Prekajski. Short communication from the Institute of Chemistry of the Faculty of Science on the chemical investigation of the active substance from the female gypsy moth. *Zashtita Bilja* (*Pest Control*), no. **52–53**, 176 (1959).

323. Stein, G. Über den Sexuallockstoff von Hummelmännchen. *Naturwissenschaften*, **50**, 305 (1963).

324. Stein, G. Untersuchungen über den Sexuallockstoff der Hummelmännchen. *Biol. Zentr.*, **82**, 345 (1963).

325. Steinbrecht, R. A. Feinstruktur und Histochemie der Sexualduftdrüse des Seidenspinners *Bombyx mori* L. *Z. Zellforsch.*, **64**, 227 (1964).

325a. Steinbrecht, R. A. Die Abhängigkeit der Lockwirkung des Sexualduftorgans weiblicher Seidenspinner (*Bombyx mori*) von Alter und Kopulation. *Z. vergl. Physiol.*, **48**, 341 (1964).

326. Steinbrecht, R. A., and D. Schneider. Die Faltung der äusseren Zellmembran in den Sexuallockstoff-Drüsenzellen des Seidenspinners. *Naturwissenschaften*, **51**, 41 (1964).

327. Sturtevant, A. H. Experiments on sex recognition and the problem of sexual selection in *Drosophila*. *J. Animal Behavior*, **5**, 351 (1915).

328. Sutton, G. P. Zygaenidae attracted by *Lasiocampa quercus* female. *Entomologist*, **55**, 280 (1922).

328a. Taschenberg, E. P., *Die Insekten, Tausendfüssler und Spinnen*, in Brehm's *Tierleben*, 2nd Ed., Verlag Bibliographischen Instituts, Leipzig, Vol. 9, 1877, p. 75.

329. Teudt, H. Eine Erklärung der Geruchserscheinungen. *Biol. Centrbl.*, **33**, 716 (1913).

330. Tinbergen, N. An objectivistic study of the innate behaviour of animals. *Bibliotheca Biotheoretica*, [D], **1**, 98 pp. (1942).

331. Tinbergen, N., *Social Behaviour in Animals*, Methuen and Co., London, 1953, p. 150.

332. Titschack, E. Beiträge zu einer Monographie der Kleidermotte, *Tineola biselliella* Hum. *Z. tech. Biol.*, **10**, 1 (1922).

333. Travis, B. V. Habits of the June beetle, *Phyllophaga lanceolata* (Say) in Iowa. *J. Econ. Entomol.*, **32**, 690 (1939).

334. Truscheit, E., and K. Eiter. Synthese der vier isomeren Hexadecadien-(10.12)-ole-(1). *Ann.*, **658**, 65 (1962).

335. Truscheit, E., and K. Eiter. Ungesättigte aliphatische Alkoholen. Ger. Patent 1,163,313 (Feb. 20, 1964).

336. Truscheit, E., K. Eiter, A. Butenandt, and E. Hecker. Verfahren zur Herstellung sterisch einheitlicher Dien-(10,12)-ole-(1). Austrian Patent 223,182 (Sept. 10, 1962).

337. Truscheit, E., K. Eiter, A. Butenandt, and E. Hecker. Verfahren zur Herstellung von 10-trans, 12-cis- oder 10-cis,12-cis-Dien-(10,12)-olen-(1). Ger. Patent 1,138,037 (Oct. 18, 1962).

338. Truscheit, E., G. Haberland, W. Puls, and K. Schlossmann. 10-Hydroxy-7-hexadecyn-1-oic acid. French Patent 1,357,951 (Apr. 10, 1964).

339. Urbahn, E. Abdominale Duftorgane bei weiblichen Schmetterlingen. *Jena. Z. Naturwiss.*, **59**, 277 (1913).

340. Valentine, J. M. The olfactory sense of the adult mealworm beetle *Tenebrio molitor* (Linn.). *J. Exptl. Zool.*, **58**, 165 (1931).

340a. Vité, J. P., and R. I. Gara. Volatile attractants from ponderosa pine attacked by bark beetles (Coleoptera, Scolytidae). *Contrib. Boyce Thompson Inst.*, **21**, 251 (1962).

341. Vité, J. P., R. I. Gara, and R. A. Kliefoth. Collection and bioassay of a volatile fraction attractive to *Ips confusus* (Lec.) (Coleoptera: Scolytidae). *Contrib. Boyce Thompson Inst.*, **22**, 39 (1963).

341a. Vité, J. P., R. I. Gara, and H. D. von Scheller. Field observations on the response to attractants of bark beetles infesting southern pines. *Contrib. Boyce Thompson Inst.*, **22**, 461 (1964).

342. Vogel, R. Zur Kenntnis der Geruchsorgane der Wespen und Bienen. *Zool. Anz.*, **53**, 20 (1921).

343. Vogel, S. Das sexuelle Anlockungsprinzip der Catasetinen- und Stanhopeen-Blüten und die wahre Funktion ihres sogenannten Futtergewebes. *Österr. botan. Z.*, **110**, 308 (1963).

344. Vöhringer, K. Zur Biologie der grossen Wachsmotte (*Galleria mellonella* L.), III: Morphologische und biologische Untersuchungen am Falter der grossen Wachsmotte (*Galleria mellonella* L.). *Zool. Jahrb., Abt. Anat. Ontog. Tiere*, **58**, 275 (1934).

345. Wagner, W. Anlockung der Schlupfwespen-Männchen durch Weibchen, die noch im Cocon sassen. *Z. wiss. Insektenbiol.*, **5**, 245 (1909).

345a. Wakabayashi, N., unpublished results.

345b. Waters, R. M., and M. Jacobson. Attractiveness of gyplure masked by impurities. *J. Econ. Entomol.*, **58**, 370 (1965).

346. Weismann, A. Über Duftschuppen. *Zool. Anz.*, **1**, 98 (1878).

347. Wharton, D. R. A., E. D. Black, and C. Merritt, Jr. Sex attractant of the American cockroach. *Science*, **142**, 1257 (1963).

348. Wharton, D. R. A., E. D. Black, C. Merritt, Jr., M. L. Wharton, M. Bazinet, and J. T. Walsh. Isolation of the sex attractant of the American cockroach. *Science*, **137**, 1062 (1962).

349. Wharton, D. R. A., G. L. Miller, and M. L. Wharton. The odorous attractant of the American cockroach, *Periplaneta americana* (L.), I: Quantitative aspects of the response to the attractant. *J. Gen. Physiol.*, **37**, 461 (1954).

350. Wharton, D. R. A., G. L. Miller, and M. L. Wharton. The odorous attractant of the American cockroach, *Periplaneta americana* (L.),

II: A bioassay method for the attractant. *J. Gen. Physiol.*, **37**, 471 (1954).

351. Wharton, M. L., and D. R. A. Wharton. The production of sex attractant substance and of oöthecae by the normal and irradiated American cockroach, *Periplaneta americana* L. *J. Insect Physiol.*, **1**, 229 (1957).

352. Whiting, P. W. Reproductive reactions of sex mosaics of a parasitic wasp, *Habrobracon juglandis*. *J. Comp. Psychol.*, **14**, 345 (1932).

353. Willcocks, F. C., *The Insects and Related Pests of Egypt*, Cairo, Egypt, Vol. 1, Part 2, 1937, p. 546.

354. Wilson, E. O. Pheromones. *Sci. American*, **208** (5), 100 (1963).

354a. Wilson, E. O., and W. H. Bossert. Chemical communication among animals. *Recent Progr. in Hormone Research*, **19**, 673 (1963).

355. Withycombe, C. L. Notes on the biology of some British neuroptera (Planipennia). *Trans. Entomol. Soc. London*, **1922**, 501.

356. Wood, D. L. The attraction created by males of a bark beetle *Ips confusus* (LeConte) attacking ponderosa pine (Coleoptera: Scolytidae). *Pan-Pacific Entomologist*, **38**, 141 (1962).

356a. Wood, D. L., and J. P. Vité. Studies on the host selection behavior of *Ips confusus* (LeConte) (Coleoptera, Scolytidae) attacking *Pinus ponderosa*. *Contrib. Boyce Thompson Inst.*, **21**, 79 (1961).

357. Wray, C., and M. H. Farrier. Response of the Nantucket pine tip moth to attractants. *J. Econ. Entomol.*, **56**, 714 (1963).

358. Wright, R. H. Odour and chemical constitution. *Nature*, **173**, 831 (1954).

359. Wright, R. H. A theory of olfaction and of the action of mosquito repellent. *Can. Entomologist*, **89**, 518 (1957).

360. Wright, R. H. The olfactory guidance of flying insects. *Can. Entomologist*, **90**, 81 (1958).

361. Wright, R. H. How insects follow a scent. *New Scientist*, **14**, 339 (1962).

362. Wright, R. H. Molecular vibration and insect sex attractants. *Nature*, **198**, 455 (1963).

363. Wright, R. H. Insect control by nontoxic means. *Science*, **144**, 487 (1964).

364. Wright, R. H. Olfactory guidance of insects. *Can. Entomologist*, **96**, 146 (1964).

365. Wright, R. H. Odor and molecular vibration: the far infrared spectra of some perfume chemicals. *Ann. N. Y. Acad. Sci.*, **116**, 552 (1964).

365a. Wright, R. H. *The Science of Smell*, Basic Books, New York, 1964.

365b. Wright, R. H. After pesticides—what? *Nature*, **204**, 121 (1964).

365c. Wright, R. H. "Metarchon," a new term for a class of nontoxic pest control agents. *Nature*, **204**, 603 (1964).

366. Yamamoto, R. Collection of the sex attractant from female American cockroaches. *J. Econ. Entomol.*, **56**, 119 (1963).

367. Zayed, S. M. A. D., T. M. Hussein, and I. M. I. Fakr. Über den Sexuallockstoff des Baumwollwurms (*Prodenia litura* F.) *Z. Naturforsch.*, **18b**, 265 (1963).

368. Zehmen, H. v. Ein Beitrag zur Frage der Anlockstoffe weiblicher Falterschädlinge. *Centrbl. ges. Forstw.*, **68**, 57 (1942).

369. Zmarlicki, C., and R. A. Morse. Queen mating. Drones apparently congregate in certain areas to which queens fly to mate. *Am. Bee J.*, **103**, 414 (1963).

INDEX

147